STO✓

He-Who-Runs-Far

He-Who-Runs-Far

By Hazel Fredericksen

Illustrations by John Houser

Young Scott Books

New York

TABLE OF CONTENTS

Indian World

1. To a New Beginning

It was dusk when they reached Oidak, but even in the half-light Pablo could see this Arizona Indian village was not like his. It had more houses, and many of them were made of adobe bricks like those he had seen at the trading post at Sells on the way here.

The car stopped at a path that led to one of the adobe houses. When they got out, Pablo followed his grandmother to the house. She went up a step and opened the door. Pablo did not enter at once; he was looking up at the roof, which was shining now in the early light of the moon.

Tall Bear, right behind him, explained, "The roof is made of tin."

What is tin? wondered Pablo. How does it feel to touch? Where does it come from, and how is it fastened to the top of the house? So many things Pablo wanted to know, but he only looked up at his grandfather and nodded.

This grandfather was almost a stranger to him. Pablo had always known that Tall Bear was the father of his mother and that Shining Leaf was her mother, but the rugged distance between this village and little Pa Vi, where Pablo had always lived, had kept the boy from knowing them. He noticed, especially now, how tall this white-haired grandparent was, how straight he stood and how he carried his broad shoulders high. Pablo pulled his own shoulders back, and followed his grandmother inside.

She reached up and pulled a hanging cord. Bright light struck everything in the room. Pablo blinked and looked toward the open door, expecting to see lightning although there had been no sign of a storm.

"This is an electric light," Shining Leaf said. "There is a big electric line near here and the council of our village has spent money to bring the lights to our homes."

Pablo, his eyes getting used to the light, found that he was in a room with two glass windows. "These let daylight come in but keep out the bugs and the birds and the cold," said Shining Leaf. The room had a floor all of wood, with a bright rug on it, a wooden table to eat from, and wooden chairs to sit on. Shining Leaf explained the working of the square stove, made of iron, how she kindled and lighted it, how it heated the house in winter, how she cooked on it all year round.

Pablo was bewildered by all these unusual things. He had been taught not to ask prying questions, but his curiosity did not escape Tall Bear's notice.

"When you are old enough to have a home of your own you may want one like this," the grandfather said. "Some of our people like this kind, and some like the kind your mother and father have."

"The roof," Pablo said. "Does it keep dirt from falling on the floor even when it rains?"

"Yes, and it is easy to keep this wooden floor clean. Your mother, with her dirt floor, has to sweep and sprinkle it every day."

Shining Leaf opened a little iron door in the side of the stove, thrust in some twigs and lighted them with a match. They snapped in the fire, and Shining Leaf added some larger pieces of wood and closed the little iron door. Soon Pablo was feeling the pleasant glow of heat, while his grandmother was warming some mush in a pot on the stove.

Shining Leaf drew a chair to the table. "You may sit on this while you eat."

Pablo sat down on the very edge of the chair, warily. So many unfamiliar things!

When Pablo had finished his mush, his grandmother said, "Come, you will sleep in our other room." Pablo followed her through a door into a smaller room where she flicked on another light to reveal a single window. This room had a bed with a blanket spread upon it; it yielded to a light pressure of Shining Leaf's hand. "Springs," she said.

"Before you go to sleep, pull this cord to turn the light off." As she turned to leave, Shining Leaf stooped and gave Pablo's shoulder a reassuring pat.

Pablo, left alone, looked uneasily at the light. He reached up and gave the cord a tug. The bright light went out. He pulled the cord again and the light flashed on. He did this several times. It gave him a feeling of mastery.

Then he looked awhile at the bed. He backed against it, carefully swung one leg onto the blanket, caught hold of the springs to help pull his other leg up, and lay down. He turned his body very gingerly to see what would happen, and felt a slight rocking motion.

To a New Beginning

He lay very still and looked up at the sky-tight ceiling. In the summer he had always slept where he could see the stars. Even in winter, when he slept indoors, he could see the light of the moon through the occasional spaces in the branches that thatched the roof. He wished very much that he could sleep out of doors this night, and his thoughts flew miles across the reservation to his home in his isolated village in the mountains.

Right now his mother, father, Younger Brother and Sister would be sleeping on the ground in the arbor-like ramada. Small Dog would be curled up by them or softly padding around looking for tasty bits of leftover tortillas. Friendly coyotes would be singing in the distance. A few mesquite coals would still be glowing in the cook-fire, and their smell would be pungent in the air. He sighed, pulled the cord once more and the light went off. But sleep would not come.

Too many things had happened that day to let him forget by merely closing his eyes. He turned over restlessly—and the springs jumped. He decided that even though he could not sleep out of doors here he would not have to sleep on this wiggly bed. He edged off the bed, spread the blanket on the floor and curled up on it.

2. The Home of Yesterday

It was long before he got to sleep. It all had happened so suddenly.

Yesterday morning Pablo had come as usual, into the family ramada at Pa Vi, fresh from his sleep outdoors. He had sniffed happily at the breakfast smells. Slices of bread were frying golden brown in the cooking pan over the small mesquite fire. Coffee was bubbling in a smoke-blackened pot hung on a rod above the fire. Pablo's mother, Gray Owl, with other members of the family, squatted on the ground close to the cook-fire, already eating.

Red Deer, Pablo's father, thickset, brownskinned, grinned at slim Pablo when he saw they were dressed alike: red cotton shirts and blue jeans. Small Dog wagged his tail joyfully.

The Home of Yesterday

"Hello, Small Dog," Pablo said, patting him. As he ate, the boy now and then gave the pet a morsel of fried bread from his dish. Now and then, too, he would glance up to look toward the sun rising over the mountain foothills that straggled down to the village edge.

Red Deer said quietly, "Finish eating your breakfast, Older Son. We have much to do today. You can help your mother pack what we need to take with us to summer camp tomorrow."

It seemed the beginning of the usual simple, friendly day in the Papago village of Pa Vi.

In late spring of each year the people of Pa Vi, a mountain village with no space for planting, would pile goods into their wagons and, taking along seeds to plant, would ride many miles to a special, fertile place in the lower desert which they called their summer camp. There they had ramadas which they kept in repair for living quarters. Through the hot summer and into fall they would plant, grow, and harvest corn and beans, and bring them back, along with fruits, herbs and other desert plants, to their mountain home where they lived through the rest of the year because here was shelter from the cruel desert winds and sometimes small game to hunt during the winter months.

3. The Keeper of the Smoke

Then, when Gray Owl was cooking the evening meal, a team and wagon drew up in front of the ramada. No one recognized the driver as he climbed down off the wagon. But when he was followed more slowly by an older woman and man, Pablo saw his mother look up in disbelief. Then laughing gaily she ran forward in welcome.

"My father! My mother!" she called.

In a few minutes Pablo, Younger Brother, and Younger Sister had met their grandparents for the first time. And the grandparents had been reunited with their daughter, Gray Owl, and her husband, Red Deer. And now they met Red Deer's uncle, Black Fox.

The driver was introduced as Little Badger, a sturdy Papago from Oidak. He had volunteered to bring Tall Bear and Shining Leaf to Pa Vi for this visit. He had driven his car first to the trading post at Sells, where the government had its Papago agency. There he had to borrow a team and wagon to bring them over the rough road to Pa Vi.

Gray Owl put additional food into the cooking pot and soon the family sat down together in the ramada and shared the meal. There was talk about many things and there was laughter, but there was also something very serious in the air.

As the talk continued the children were sent, one by one, away from the firelight to their sleeping blankets—Pablo, the oldest, last of all, when the grown ones said he must be tired and would need much sleep before tomorrow. But if they thought he would fall asleep at once they were mistaken. Pablo watched from under his blanket, and strained to hear every word he could.

Some of the things he heard were not new to him. He knew that his mother was the only child of Tall Bear and Shining Leaf. She had lived with them in Oidak until she married Red Deer. But Pablo had not known that once his mother had gone to the Big School where they taught in English.

Pablo saw Black Fox question her with his eyes,

and he heard her say: "It is true, what my father says. I did go for a while to the government Indian school in the big city outside our reservation." Then, almost in a whisper, she added, "After I came to Pa Vi, I forgot what I did not wish to remember."

For a while no one said anything. Then Tall Bear said abruptly, "Older Son is eleven, yet he cannot understand any English words. He is not a stupid boy. Why hasn't he learned some English, the way all the boys at Oidak do?"

Red Deer replied softly to Tall Bear, "Black Fox does not wish the people of our village to learn any English. That is the language of the white man."

That, thought Pablo, would settle it. Had not the decision about English been spoken by the voice of Black Fox—the voice that soared strong and clear in the sunrise chant and gave the day's announcements? No one ever questioned or disagreed with Black Fox. Pablo listened closely to what Tall Bear might say.

For a few minutes Tall Bear sat motionless with bowed head. "Our people have to work with the white man and trade with him," he said without looking at Black Fox.

Again he spoke. "Red Deer, father of my grand-children," he said, "I am an old man. Each year it is harder for me to tend my gardens and take care of my duties as Governor and Keeper-of-the-Smoke at Oidak. I have no child to help me. You have three. I have come, just before you go to your summer camp, to say 'Let me take Older Son back with me to Oidak.' "

There was surprised silence.

The grandfather went on: "Older Son can help me in my gardens. I will give him the legends of our people as my grandfather gave them to me many years ago. I will teach him the ritual of the rain and the ceremony of the Keeper-of-the-Smoke."

Pablo hardly breathed, waiting for his father to speak. His mother sat with eyes downcast.

His grandfather resumed in a lowered voice: "Someday this grandson may be Governor of the village of Oidak and Keeper-of-the-Smoke. The choice of a successor will be mine. My people will accept my choice. But to be a leader, helping his people, he must learn how to talk to the white man in his language. He must learn English and also the white man's magic." Tall Bear raised his voice a little. "For this, he must go to the Big School."

21

After these words of challenge Pablo lay trembling, afraid of what might come next.

He saw Black Fox plant himself in front of Tall Bear and heard him say: "I have heard what you said, father-of-my-nephew's wife. I answer that we do not want Older Son to become like the white man. We see white people at the trading post who point their fingers. That is immodest. They push and shove. That is rude. They boldly speak out. That is impolite. They laugh at ancient ways. That is irreverent."

Tall Bear answered slowly. "I know that the ways of the white man are not all good. But learning his language will not violate the traditions and beliefs of our people. Learning the white man's magic will give my grandson power. Some boys from Oidak go to the Big School a year to learn things our day school does not teach. But even in our own day school they have learned some English. My grandson has not been taught any English. To be a leader he must learn English and much more. He must stay a second year."

Black Fox replied sharply. "The Indian who does not live in the ways of his people is not an Indian. Power is a gift from Great Spirit Eé toy, given in a dream to those worthy to receive it."

The Keeper of the Smoke

"My grandson," said Tall Bear, "will continue to be an Indian. He will think like an Indian. I have said I will teach him the old rituals, the sacred songs and legends. He will fast and do all the things that we did to earn power in the old days. But today this is not enough. Now a leader must have the power to know and understand the things done by white men who are all around us."

A crackling silence followed. To Pablo, who had never known a quarrel among his people, all this was frightening. Finally he heard Black Fox say in a deep voice, "My nephew will make the decision."

Pablo watched as his father and mother spoke to each other with their eyes. Then in a clear voice his father said: "Older Son will go with you in the morning, grandfather-of-my-children. He will follow your plan and go to the Big School."

Pablo would not forget the disdain in Black Fox's voice: "Send him away then to learn the language and thoughts of the white man. Great Spirit will be angry. Our people will suffer." With that, Black Fox turned and walked out of the ramada. It had almost seemed to Pablo then that a great friend was walking out of his life.

4. The Long Desert Journey

What he had overheard last night had happened to Pablo today. Before the sun could light up the Pa Vi cactus tops, Gray Owl had tapped him lightly on the shoulder.

She said, "Get up, my son. You are not going to summer camp with us. Today you will go with your grandfather and grandmother to their village of Oidak. There, in the months of the hot moons, you will help your grandfather. And he will teach you about the beginnings of our people. After the crops are harvested, you will go for two years to the big Indian school in the white man's city."

She showed no sign of worry as she broke the news to him.

She did not ask Pablo how he felt about this. She did not seem to expect any questions. She merely

24

handed Pablo a clean pair of blue jeans and a new red shirt and he started to put them on. Nothing was said by mother or by son as to whether they expected to see each other again before Pablo would end his learning at the Big School. Both of them were accepting a Papago decision in a Papago way.

As Pablo put on his clean clothes, he watched his mother cooking breakfast. Then he joined the others squatting, waiting to eat. His father grinned at him. Gray Owl came over, put a hand on Pablo's shoulder and looked deeply into his eyes.

"You will see the village where I used to live," she smiled. "You will stay in a house with windows. You may even see the place in the hills where I used to get devil's claw for making baskets."

Breakfast was hardly over when Little Badger brought up the team and wagon. He was ready for the long trip to Oidak.

From the house across the road came Black Fox, his white hair blowing against his yellow-brown skin. He looked searchingly at Pablo. Then he turned to look at Pablo's father. "Older Son is going?"

Red Deer nodded.

No one else spoke. Little Badger looked straight ahead as if he had not heard. With a shrug, Black Fox left and walked rapidly toward his house. Pablo wished for just one smile, but Black Fox did not look back.

Pablo and his grandparents climbed into the wagon. Eight-year-old Younger Brother and four-year-old Younger Sister, accustomed to going wherever Pablo went, ran to join him in the wagon, but Gray Owl firmly brought them back to stand by her. "No, you will ride in another wagon to summer camp," she said. "Older Brother is going to Oidak."

Red Deer lifted Younger Sister to his shoulders and gently slipped his fingers around the small hand of Younger Brother. Small Dog stood next to Younger Brother, trying to decide what was expected of him.

Little Badger clucked softly to the horses, and in the usual quiet Indian way, without farewells, they were on their way, Pablo's family watching with somber eyes.

The team was soon raising dust as it meandered through greasewood and cactus, following a road that was little more than wheel tracks. Hours later they reached a graveled road.

"We are coming to Sells; the road is better," Little Badger said.

Grandfather smiled. "Black Fox does not want good roads. He says they will bring unwanted white people to Pa Vi. They would try to change old customs. He does not want people of his village to hear or speak English words. He believes that if an English school came to his village, children would be taught to question beliefs of their ancestors and the authority of their elders."

A short silence. Then Little Badger asked, "Is Pa Vi the only village left on our reservation where people still live in round grass-thatched houses?"

"No," answered Grandfather. "There is one other village where a man like Black Fox opposes any change. The sixty-eight other villages gave up that kind of house long ago."

"Those are the only two villages, aren't they, that have summer camps?"

"Yes," Grandfather said, "the people of these two villages like the shelter and privacy the mountains give, but since there is no room to raise food there, they must move to the valley and stay in their summer camps. Their children move back and forth about every six new moons and don't have a chance to learn of things that happen in other villages. My grandson has learned from his father, in summer camp, how to hoe, plant, weed, and harvest crops. Now after he helps me in my gardens he will go away to the Big School."

Little Badger nodded, then commented, "I hear that when a boy goes to the Big School the school doesn't want him to visit the reservation again as long as he is learning. How long will your grandson stay there?"

"I have said two years. Some stay a year—some even less time. Some try to run away, but the school always catches them, and takes them back. I want grandson to learn many things to help our people. After two years he will come back to live in Oidak, learn, and help me with my duties."

Little Badger looked keenly at Tall Bear. "With the duties of Governor and Keeper-of-the-Smoke?" he asked quietly.

Tall Bear nodded.

Miles later the course through the desert cacti was interrupted as the gravel road ended at Sells. Pablo saw, for the first time, a place larger than Pa Vi. It had a square adobe office building with an American flag flying over it. Near was a larger building that Little Badger said was a "government day school." Then there were a half-dozen large adobe houses, partly hidden by trees taller than any Pablo had ever seen, and many more houses, much smaller, that were scattered over the landscape—homes where people lived. But he saw no round grass-thatched houses such as he knew. Not far from the American flag were a couple of buildings. Tall Bear called them "stores, where you can buy things."

Little Badger had given them no time for sightseeing. They still had far to go. He drove the team directly to the rear yard of one of the smaller houses, left the wagon and its team and transferred his passengers to a blue vehicle waiting there.

He put Pablo in the back seat with Shining Leaf, climbed into the front seat with Tall Bear. In no time he was turning a wheel with his hands, while doing something else with his feet. There was a roar and a lurch. The car started, flinging the passengers against their seatbacks.

Shining Leaf quickly reassured Pablo. "This is Little Badger's automobile," she said. "He will take us to Oidak in this car over a good road."

Soon the car seemed to be flying past cacti and trees. We move like a roadrunner, Pablo thought; then he whispered, "What makes this wagon move?"

Shining Leaf answered softly, "Gasoline—they put it inside the car." Pablo did not understand, but politeness forbade more questions, so he settled down to watch the countryside speed by.

The farther they traveled, the sharper the changes. Pablo had discovered kinds of cacti that always seemed to grow separate from one another around Pa Vi. These were often clumped together here—as though they learned they must live together. Yet some of the plants, like the greasewood, still managed to grow the same way they did at home. The strange things he saw here made him realize how he had grown to love the familiar things at home.

Pablo had felt no great wrench at leaving his family. Among Papagos it was thought natural for a child to live with his grandparents, aunts or uncles, if they asked for him, even though he did not know them. But Pablo had felt deeply—and a little scared—about leaving Pa Vi, the only place he had ever known.

And now he lay on the blanket on the bedroom floor in this strange house, with a light that pulled on and the bedsprings that sprang. To think that only the night before he had been in Pa Vi, ready for the familiar annual trip to summer camp.

5. Two Languages

At breakfast next morning, eating at the table in the main room, Tall Bear asked Pablo kindly, "Did you like your bed?"

Pablo looked down, gathered courage. He said, "I didn't sleep on the bed, my grandfather. The springs were too jumpy. I slept on the floor."

Tall Bear laughed. "Would you like to sleep outdoors?"

"Oh, yes. Beside the house. Could I sleep there on my blanket?"

"I'll get you a canvas blanket. That will be better in the sand."

After breakfast Tall Bear said, "Come, my grandson, we will go to the gardens before the sun warms the earth too much."

When Pablo and his grandfather reached the

gardens, Pablo saw that here too every family had a plot of ground where they raised corn and beans which they tended until the harvest in the fall just as the people of Pa Vi did in their summer camp.

Pablo saw only older men like his grandfather and younger boys like himself working here. Younger men and older boys, Tall Bear explained, had cattle to look after in the mountain ranges if they had not sought work off the reservation.

When the sun stood directly overhead and the day was near its hottest, the workday in the gardens ended, and everyone walked home for lunch. Pablo found that the food was almost the same as he had known in Pa Vi, but sometimes in addition to fried bread, corn mush, and beans, his grandmother made something of cholla buds she called "salad." And occasionally there was meat of the cow cooked in a big pot on the stove. This was called "beef." These things Pablo had never had in Pa Vi.

After lunch Tall Bear sat under the shadow of the big mesquite tree that grew beside the house. Here some men of the council joined him for advice and thoughtful discussions.

Pablo was free to look around the village. He found boys he had seen in the gardens during the morning. They were all playing games together. This puzzled him. In his village children played only with others who were blood relatives.

He watched shyly from a distance but could not get the meaning of their games. One boy called to him. Pablo did not understand him. Then the boy called in the Papago language and Pablo walked slowly toward the group.

"Don't you know English?" this boy asked in the Papago language.

"A few words," Pablo replied.

The boys talked this over in English. Then in Papago: "Have you never been to school?"

When he said he had been to school, but had not been taught English, they looked at him. Again they spoke together in English. From their sidelong glances Pablo knew they thought he was not telling the truth.

"What kind of school was that?" said one. "They always teach English in school."

"Not in Pa Vi, my village," said Pablo. "I just came here to live with my grandfather."

The boy who had first spoken in Papago asked, "Is the Governor of our village really your grandfather?" Pablo nodded.

Again the boys talked together. They shook

their heads and the first boy said, "The Governor speaks and understands English. If he were your grandfather, he would have taught you."

Pablo answered quietly. "It is not English he is teaching me. He is teaching me things I need to know so that some day I might take his place in this village."

The boys looked at Pablo in surprise and disbelief, then broke into derisive laughter.

Pablo swallowed, clenched his fists, and turned back to his grandfather's house. As he walked he put his feet down hard. Some day, as Keeper-of-the-Smoke and Governor of this village, he would walk out in the morning dawn to say prayers to Eé toy, make announcements, and assign the village people to their labors—even these boys now so smugly playing their games.

From that day the boys made no further advances toward Pablo. He had to find things to do by himself in the long afternoons. He went off by himself on long walks. Sometimes he ran across the hot sandy desert.

6. Legends and Stories

In the leisure of dusk Tall Bear said, "Sit down here, my grandson. Now I will tell you of our people, the Papagos.

"The Papago people do not have a written language, so you must learn our history and legends from the older men of the tribe who know them. You must keep them in your heart and mind.

"In the long ago before there were any Papago people there was Eé toy, Great Spirit, who knows all things. He knew that some day water would come and cover the whole earth. So he wove himself a big watertight basket, and when the water came he stayed inside it. When the water went down enough he got out and walked around. But he found the ground was floating around in the water and would not stay in one place.

"He studied about it. What should he do? Finally he thought of a plan. He called the spiders to come and weave the land together with their webs. They worked very hard, but when they had finished there were still spots where the webs were not strong enough to hold the land together. Great Spirit told the spiders he was satisfied with their work. He would call those places of water 'oceans' and 'lakes.'

" 'This place where I now stand,' he told the spiders, 'is the center of the world. This shall be the place of *Tohono au autam*—Desert People.'

"When he said this there were no desert people, so he began making them out of mud left by the waters. When he had enough he stood them all in a row and asked them to speak, and they did. Then he told them to stay here always at the center of the earth. They have obeyed him, and Great Spirit watches over them from his home on Baboquivari, so close to us here."

Pablo looked up at Baboquivari. It could be seen from all parts of Papagoland, and Pablo had gazed on it in awe countless times from far-off Pa Vi. Its upper part is a rock dome with sides running almost straight up for 1200 feet, then rounded off to a flat top. From the desert it looks like a giant castle. Eé toy, on the top, would be 700 feet higher than the mountains all around, and able to watch all of his people.

"Does Great Spirit live all by himself up there?" Pablo asked.

"Wind Man and Cloud Man live there when they are at home, but Eé toy often sends them far away to give coolness and rain to thirsty land."

Pablo sighed. So much to learn if you listened to catch every word. Tall Bear must have noticed the worry in Pablo's eyes. He said, "My grand-child, you have heard enough for now. The stars are out and it is time for you to sleep."

Pablo curled up on his canvas blanket out un-der the stars and looked toward Baboquivari un-til his eyes closed in sleep.

o   o   o

At near dusk the next day, Pablo saw his grand-father sitting by the side of the house, his eyes fixed on majestic Baboquivari. Pablo sidled close to him but did not speak. Tall Bear moved over. Pablo sat down beside him, waiting for another legend.

Tall Bear began. "Long, long ago our people

did not know how to plant crops, build houses, or make dishes and baskets. So Eé toy taught them to use wet mud to make cooking pots and dishes. Once as Eé toy dug into the side of a hill to get clay for dishes, Coyote watched him. After Eé toy had taken out the clay, Coyote jumped into the hole and said, 'This is a house for me.' Ever since then Coyote has dug into the side of a hill to make his home."

Tall Bear paused and exchanged smiles with Pablo. "Our people too lived in holes they had dug in the side of a hill. But one family did not like it, so they built for themselves a little round grass house.

"When Eé toy came and saw they were trying to build a house, he said he would show them how to cut stalks of ocotillo cactus, set them in the ground, fasten them together with ribs of saguaro, and put branches of mesquite and creosote bushes over the top to make a roof.

"He saw how the women used grasses and willow sticks to make baskets, but these baskets were all alike, so no woman knew which were her own. He went back to his home in Baboquivari and brought the plant we call 'devil's claw.' He showed the women how they could use parts of this plant to weave designs so each would have her own mark on the basket she made."

Pablo forgot he was listening. He broke in: "My mother does that. But the devil's claw plant is now very hard to find."

Tall Bear nodded. "Once these plants spread from the foothills of Baboquivari nearly to the edge of this village. They were dug up to make room for crops, but I think devil's claw grows in the foothills."

Tall Bear was silent, and although his eyes were turned toward Pablo, he seemed to be looking at something far away. When he spoke again his voice was soft and husky. "Long ago, when your mother was not much older than you are now, she sat here in the shade of this old mesquite tree weaving baskets."

He smiled and laid his hand gently against the trunk of the old tree. "She was a thin little girl with hair hanging almost to her waist. Your grandmother taught her to weave baskets of willow and sweet grass, to use devil's claw to weave a design in the baskets. She learned, too, how to make pots and dishes of clay dug from the wash." Tall Bear chuckled. "Her dishes were never very good—she didn't like to work with the wet clay—

but her baskets were fine. Older women could not make storage baskets more watertight than hers. Her designs were different from any others in the village."

Tall Bear stopped, and Pablo, leaning forward and clearing his throat, asked a question that had nagged him since the night he learned Gray Owl had been to the Big School. "When my mother came back from the Big School, did she know about the magic of the white man?"

Tall Bear looked speculatively at Pablo. He said, "No. Your mother only went to the Big School from the months of Ghost Face until Green Leaves (January to June). In those days the government school let boys and girls come back to their villages each summer to help in the fields. The bus from the Big School went only to the trading post at Sells. Parents had to go there to get their boys and girls when they came back.

"The day your mother and the others came back was the first day of the cactus festival at Sells. Parents and children stayed on to enjoy the four days of celebration and prayers to Great Spirit for rain." Tall Bear stopped, and seemed lost in his thoughts for a while. Pablo waited silently.

"Then, just as now," Tall Bear continued,

"there was much food, and cactus syrup to drink, and always a few people walked or rode many miles to join others in the celebration."

The cactus festival—Pablo sat very still—this year he would miss this happy time at their summer camp. He wondered whether Younger Brother was tall enough and strong enough now to use the long picking stick to get the ripe red fruits from the tops of the high saguaros. He licked his lips as he thought of the sweet red pulp and juice. He hoped Younger Brother and Younger Sister would remember, after eating the fruit, to throw the shell down red-side up to encourage rain. Would there be lots of juice this year for the women to cook into syrup to be drunk by the people praying for rain? Would rain come as soon as the rain songs and prayers were over? Would there be lots of slick mud to wade through in the gardens after the rain? Suddenly Pablo was aware that his grandfather had stopped talking and was watching him.

"I am sorry, my grandfather. I was thinking of the cactus festival at our summer camp—will you tell me more about that day my mother came back from the Big School?"

A grim little smile touched Tall Bear's lips, then he continued his story. "That day your mother came from the Big School, she was full of fun and laughter. A tall slender girl of fifteen summers. She was happy to be back with her own people and joined with the others in gay dances and the fun of the celebration.

"Your father had come to Sells from his faraway village—his first trip away from Pa Vi. He was handsome and shy. The girls all asked him to be a dance partner. He chose to dance with your mother. After the celebration your mother and father decided to marry. This meant putting aside our custom of having marriages arranged by the parents. But we were satisfied because they came from different villages and were not related—a very important rule.

"Instead of going back to Oidak with us, your father and mother were married and she went with him to Pa Vi. Because of the great distance we all knew we would not see each other for many years. Just as you won't see your mother for many years. And just as I won't see you when you go to the Big School to stay. That is the way of our people. Your mother became part of her husband's family. Now her life is with them."

"My mother never went back to the Big School?" Pablo questioned.

42

"No. Married ladies do not go to the Big School."

Pablo nodded, then added softly, "I don't think Black Fox would let her go, anyway." He looked toward Baboquivari, lost in thought.

"You are tired." Tall Bear said gently. "Go to your blanket and sleep so you will be ready to greet the sun tomorrow."

But Pablo wasn't tired, just wanting privacy to think of all the things his grandfather had told him of his mother and her basket-making. A few days before his grandparents came to Pa Vi his mother had told him a secret: she planned to shape her new baskets like animals or birds—a quail or maybe a rabbit. No other basket-maker had done this, and the trader who came to Pa Vi to buy her baskets had thought her idea was fine. One thing worried her: she couldn't find enough devil's claw near Pa Vi to get the black shreds she needed to make eyes, nose, and mouth.

If she could make the kind of baskets the man wanted, she would have enough money to buy coffee, sugar, salt, and sometimes a can of tomatoes. When she told Pablo, he had promised to keep her secret and also offered to hunt for devil's claw.

7. Wisdom of Coyote

The next day as they were gathering beans together, Tall Bear said, "When the Spanish people and other Indian tribes came to our land in olden days, they found our people raising beans. They did not say our word for beans, *pah-vo*, the way we do. It sounded to them like Papago. So they called us Papago, meaning Bean People."

"Why did the Spanish come? Just to visit?"

Pablo's grandfather did not answer for a long time. Then he said, "Some Spanish soldiers came to help one time when another tribe of Indians tried to capture our land and crops, but these Spanish did not stay long. They went back south and told about our fine land; then more Spaniards came to take our land. But our people fought bravely, and the Spaniards did not get it. Our

44

people have never fought unless we had to protect our homes and our people. But when we have had to fight we have done so with courage."

Pablo had been absorbing every word. "I wonder, did the enemy ever win any battles?"

Tall Bear looked at him earnestly. "No, I don't think so, because long ago Eé toy told some of our animal friends to help us if we had to fight. The gopher has always been our friend: in war he has gnawed the arrows of those who would attack us, so that the arrows would break or the enemy would not have enough. Owls have been our friends too. They were once Papago warriors that Eé toy took to live with him. He changed them into owls so they could watch our enemy."

Pablo knew now why the big eyes of the owls could watch by night.

He asked, "And our friend and brother, Coyote, what did he do?"

Tall Bear laughed. "Brother Coyote is clever and also full of wisdom. He played tricks to decoy the enemy into traps so we could get them. Coyote has always liked to play tricks. He will sit back and laugh all night at a good joke he has played. But when our people are in trouble, he will walk close to the campfire and give them good advice."

Pablo fidgeted. He remembered something he wanted very much to tell Tall Bear. But, trained not to interrupt older people, he managed to keep still as Tall Bear continued. "Many thousand years ago, Coyote lived with the first desert people in cave places. In those places many hundreds of people lived, worked, and laughed together until Eé toy called them to go to fields that are always green where rain falls every day."

Pablo knew Eé toy had called his father's parents, Black Fox's wife, and some others in his village to these green fields. No one ever mentioned the names of people who had gone there though, for to speak their names would make them uneasy. It would call them back from green fields to dry desert.

Sometimes these people waved their beautiful colored robes over the land to help others. These colored robes were called rainbows.

Tall Bear continued: "When Eé toy called these people, he did not call Coyote to go to the green fields to live, because he enjoyed Coyote's jokes and fun. When Eé toy was tired of work, sometimes he entered Coyote's body to romp and play. Because of this he gave Coyote powers and insight beyond that of the Desert People."

Wisdom of Coyote

When his grandfather finished, Pablo burst out: "Once when I climbed in the hills above our village I saw quick movement in the bushes near a cave entrance. I got down on my knees and crawled forward carefully to find out what it was. I saw a mother coyote lying under a creosote bush. Snuggled close beside her were five baby coyotes busily nursing. Mother Coyote heard me and raised her head to look at me, but did not try to leave the spot where she was lying. Then, when one of the babies rolled against her she gave a sharp little yelp.

"I moved closer and saw her left front foot was held in the strong steel jaws of a trap. I knew I must try to get her foot loose, but I was afraid she would not know I was trying to help and would bite me. I talked gently to her until I got close enough to take hold of the edge of the trap. Then I saw she had been chewing at her foot to try to loosen it from the trap. It took all my strength to pull the trap open so I could lift her paw from between the trap jaws. She watched me closely all the time, and did not try to bite. When her foot was free she gave a sharp little cry and bit the paw. Then she licked it, nuzzled the baby coyotes, got up and slowly limped inside the dark cave.

"I watched until she had coaxed the last baby

Pablo felt himself trembling under the reprimand. He asked, "What is power, my grandfather?"

"Power is wisdom and courage."

Pablo asked, almost pleadingly, "Do you think this power may come to me, my grandfather?"

Tall Bear looked into Pablo's eyes and touched the boy's head lightly.

"There is a long time of getting ready," he said in a gentle tone. "All through the summer I will work with you and watch you. You will go to the Big School and learn. You will come back. Then I think you will be ready for fasting and running in the desert."

The boy thought that over. "Could power come to me through the voice of Coyote?" he asked.

Tall Bear pondered. "Only Eé toy can answer that."

"If power does come to me, how will I know it?" Pablo asked.

Tall Bear drew his shoulders back and looked at Pablo very soberly. "My grandson, you will know," he said. "You will know."

With that he got up and left, leaving the teaching of sacred songs for the next day.

8. The Devil's Claw

Days scurried by in August, the month of dry grass. Summer was ended. Almost all the beans had been gathered, shelled, and spread to dry in the sun. Sometimes in the early morning and in the evening, cool puffs of air nudged Pablo and Tall Bear as they worked or sat outdoors.

For weeks Pablo had worked hard to learn from Tall Bear the secret rituals and the sacred songs.

One night Tall Bear called Pablo to come to where he sat under the mesquite tree. "Three moons you have been here in this village," he said, watching the boy closely. "You have worked hard. You have listened. You have learned. Yet your grandmother tells me you have never wanted to be friends with the boys of our village."

Pablo looked down. He had not meant anyone

51

to know the struggle he had with his loneliness and his hurt pride.

"The first week I was here I watched the boys play. They called and I walked to meet them. I thought I should not have done that because none of them were brothers, sisters, or even cousins, and in Pa Vi a boy plays only with blood relatives. They asked too many questions. They had never heard of my village. They did not believe Pa Vi had any school because I could not answer their questions in English. At first they did not think you were really my grandfather."

Pablo felt anger he had pent up until now. "Some day after I come back from the Big School, I will play games and speak English better than they do. They seem to have fun playing their games, but I think I had more fun learning and remembering the legends of our people."

"It is not the Papago way to boast," Tall Bear said quietly.

Pablo looked away, then said hesitantly, "I don't understand; they are not all one family, yet they play together as friends."

Tall Bear sighed. "There are many little differences in the beliefs of the people here and in Pa Vi that I should have remembered to explain.

When we have talked together I have thought only of the things I must be sure to teach you about our people's past. But I must tell you now that we here in Oidak, and in many other villages on our reservation, believe it is right to have friends outside our own families. We must learn to make friends and enjoy talking to and listening to others."

Tall Bear put his hand on Pablo's arm. "Three days from now, you and some other boys from Oidak will leave on the bus to go to the big government Indian school. There you will make friends with many boys—not all Papagos. You will find Indian boys from many tribes. While you are at the Big School you will be like one family."

Before going outdoors to bed that night, Pablo was alone for a short while with his grandmother. "Why do some of the boys here go to the Big School and others not?" he ventured to ask her.

She hesitated, then answered, "Because many of the older men don't want the boys to go. They stand firm against pushing ahead to learn the ways of the white men. They say that Great Spirit will punish our people if they do this. Your grandfather has tried to tell them that Eé toy will not punish us for learning. He is sure that if you, grandson of the Governor and Keeper-of-the-

Smoke, go to the Big School and come back with knowledge useful to our people it will convince them. Now hurry to sleep."

When he was on his blanket and looking up at the stars, Pablo faced up to the fact that he would be leaving in just three days. He would not see his grandparents or Oidak for two whole years; someone else would have to help his grandfather in his gardens next summer.

He thought of his family at Pa Vi. Younger Brother and Sister would be older and much bigger when he would see them again. But he would be bigger too: thirteen years old after two years in the Big School.

Would his father and mother change much before then? Now he remembered, with a start, his promise to help his mother find devil's claw pods for her basket work—the long green finger claws that would be dried black and stripped of their useful fibers. How could he get these in the little time left him before going to the Big School?

From what his grandfather had told him, he thought he could find enough devil's claw still growing in the foothills below Baboquivari. If he could get the pods he could ask to have them taken to Sells when someone went there to trade. From there someone could take them to his mother at Pa Vi.

He worked out a plan for getting the devil's claw and still keeping his mother's secret. To-morrow, during his grandfather's rest and nap, Pablo would hurry into the foothills and find devil's claw. He would be back with the pods before the evening meal. Having decided, he gave himself over to sleep.

9. The Mountain

∞∞∞

In the fields the next morning as they cleared away the last of the bean vines, Tall Bear twice noticed Pablo looking toward Baboquivari. "You are remembering what I told you about Eé toy up there. That is good, but don't forget the work here."

Pablo said, "Yes, my grandfather," and bent to gather up more vines.

Right after lunch Tall Bear settled down under the mesquite tree for his nap, and Shining Leaf went to help a neighbor shell beans. This left Pablo free to carry out his plan. He found a gunnysack to hold devil's claw pods, and a stout piece of string to tie up the sack.

With these he set off at a lively clip, humming the tune of a sacred song he had learned, sure he could get back in time for supper. I will practice running, he thought, so when the time comes I can run fast in the desert.

The trail wound up one side of some hummocks and slid down the other. It swung around, turned and seemed to cut back, growing harder to follow. It was also getting steeper, and Pablo had to stop humming to save his breath for climbing. A few times he stopped to rest. At last he came to a spring where he was glad to drop down and drink of the cool water. The trail ended here, but a clear little stream came down past the spring and Pablo thought it must be farther up this stream that the devil's claw grew.

He started along the stream-bed and climbed up and up on its twisting course, sometimes walking beside the stream and sometimes forced to walk in it when big boulders blocked his way.

At a bend where he stopped to rest, he looked up. There on a ledge of a rocky bank, high above him and a little to the right, he saw the unmistakable pods of the devil's claw.

Forgetting he was tired, he reached, caught hold of a tiny pine tree growing in the crevice of the wet, rocky cliff and straining hard, found he could pull himself up. Getting a toehold just below the little pine, he stretched for a jutting rock higher up. Grabbing this helped him climb farther. Now, out of breath, he triumphantly reached for the hard-to-find plants. He could just break their nearest slender pods.

Soon he had all he could take from where he stood, but on the ledges above him he could see many more. Could he reach them? He dropped the gathered pods into his gunnysack and tied this to his shoulders. Now both hands were free for climbing.

Feeling his way up the slippery wet rocks, grasping whatever he could, he climbed onto a thin ledge with no handhold above it. Then on hands and knees he worked his way slowly around a jutting wall of rock. Beyond that there was nothing to cling to but a small pine tree that stuck out, its branches all askew.

Carefully balancing himself, he stood up. The tree was just beyond his reach. He stretched out on tiptoes. Could he grasp it if he jumped a little? He missed it. He missed again. As he dropped back, the thin rock under his feet gave way.

Now he was plunging down the rough side of the bank, grabbing in terror at any small bushes that might stop his fall, making a tornado of dust and rock that scraped him as he went. Snatching desperately, he got a good, but prickly grip on a scrubby pine, but it came out by the roots.

Finally one did seem to hold him, but above he heard a rushing and thumping. A large dislodged rock was rolling down upon him. The smack filled his head with pain and he was crashing down.

o   o   o

When Pablo opened his eyes it was almost dark. He was on his back. He turned his head. It ached. His legs and back hurt too. With his right hand he groped carefully to find something to hold onto. He felt a small bush, took a tight grip on it, and ever so painfully pulled himself up so he could sit. In the fading light he looked around. He found he was on the side of a brushy canyon, and above him yellow cliffs rose straight into the sky. What had happened? It took him minutes to remember.

His grandparents must have missed him by now. They were probably searching for him. But they would have no idea where he had gone or where to look. How can I get back to my grandfather's house? thought Pablo.

He gathered himself slowly to get up on his feet. He was wobbly. He started working his way down along the canyon side, through the thickly matted brush and trees. His foot loosened a stone and it clattered from rock to rock down the hillside.

He called out, "Hello-o-o-o-o-o!" His voice frightened him in the stillness, and there was no answering call.

Darkness was settling fast when Pablo reached the narrow foot of the canyon, and a wind was starting to blow. Bruised from his fall, scratched from head to foot, Pablo came out on a little flat place.

Now the wind was mounting. Soon tongues of lightning split the sky. It would be best to stay here until the storm quieted. He could barely see, in the dimness, a small scrub oak. Shivering from fear and cold, he walked to the tree and crouched close to it for shelter.

He felt a little like whimpering, but remembered his grandfather had told him that when Papagos were afraid or hurt they made up songs. Pablo easily thought of some words for a song: "Alone by the mountain, alone by the mountain." But he couldn't think of a rhythm to chant.

Spatters of rain fell upon the little oak. These turned into a downpour that drenched the oak and the ground beneath. Water raced down the bed of the canyon, and in the flashes of lightning, Pablo could see little muddy streams swirling all around him. Clasping both hands around the wet trunk of his friendly little oak, he held on tightly so he wouldn't slip down into the rushing water.

The storm stopped as suddenly as it had started, but it was some time before the swirling of water lessened.

There was a little rustle in the bushes. What could it be? He sat very still waiting for more sound.

He heard a soft whine—could it be—? Then, as a small sliver of moon peeked out of the clouds, he could see what it was. His friend, Mother Coyote, was limping toward him. She hunched down quite close to him.

Pablo reached out and whispered, "Coyote, help me."

Coyote lifted her head and wailed a long loud cry, then lowered her head and listened. From far below came an answering wail and a few short barks.

Coyote lay down, apparently satisfied, and in the faint moonlight, Pablo could see her eyes watching him.

Pablo leaned back against the tree, very sure that

Coyote would speak to him. He relaxed, and before long he thought he was hearing a soft song from Coyote—about rain marching through the corn. Pablo's head nodded—his thinking blurred.

○   ○   ○

He must have slept, because when he looked again it was daylight. Mother Coyote was still there near him and watching him.

Pablo was stiff with cold. His throat was so dry it hurt to swallow. If he only could have some of the water that had run down the gully last night.

"I must find my way home somehow," he whispered. "My grandfather must be very angry with me by now."

Mother Coyote sprang up and whined at him smartly. She trotted away a short distance. Then she stopped and looked back.

"She is trying to tell me something," thought Pablo. He struggled up and started to follow. Coyote trotted a little way—then stopped to look back as though saying, "That's right—follow me."

Was she leading him back to the village? On and on they went, over rocks, through cactus and brush. Pablo was doing his best to keep going. The heat was humid. The sun beat like a cooking fire. His head was hurting. Suddenly he found himself shivering. He staggered and fell to his knees. He crawled and grabbed on to a bush and pulled himself to his feet again.

Then he fell face down, close to a cholla. He thought the earth was rolling. Was it the springs of that bed?

The next thing he knew, water was trickling down his throat. Its cool relief almost choked him. Someone was supporting his head, holding a canteen to his lips. It was Little Badger.

10. Shaman's Magic

"Is he hurt?" he heard his grandfather's voice ask. "Are bones broken?"

"I don't think any bones are broken," Little Badger said. "I think he's sick with a bad cold."

Pablo tried to speak, but his voice was a rasp. Little Badger lifted him up and carried him through greasewood and cholla to put him in the back seat of the car. Tall Bear used his coat to cover Pablo, and he pressed close against him to warm him. He didn't seem angry with Pablo at all.

Tall Bear asked, "What was in that sack you put in the car trunk?"

Little Badger answered, "He had the sack tied across his shoulders. It was wet and heavy, but when I took it from him he grabbed for it. It had devil's claw pods in it."

When they reached Tall Bear's house in the village, women were gathered outside with Pablo's grandmother.

"Is he safe?" Shining Leaf asked.

"Yes, but he's too weak to walk. I'll carry him in."

"Our grandson is very sick," Tall Bear said. "He can't speak."

Shining Leaf knelt on the floor beside Pablo, and put her hand on his forehead. "Hot," she said. "Very hot." Then she took one of his hands in hers. "Dry as the corn husks. I think we must call the shaman, Blue Eagle."

Little Badger thought he knew where they could find Blue Eagle.

Shining Leaf now filled a small bowl with water and, kneeling beside Pablo, raised his head and guided the bowl to his lips. "Swallow, my grandson," she said softly.

Pablo let some of the cool water run down his parched throat. He smiled his gratitude, and when he had his head on the blanket, again closed his eyes.

He opened them at the sound of men's footsteps. Little Badger was back. He had brought the village medicine man.

Blue Eagle was very old, with gray hair straggling to his shoulders. He nodded to Shining Leaf and, with surprising ease for one of his years, seated himself cross-legged on a mat on the floor near Pablo. He opened a little buckskin bag he carried, took several things from it and laid them ready at hand.

Of these he first picked up four eagle feathers fastened to a little stick. He brushed the feathers lightly over Pablo's throat to wave away the evil. Next he took some sacred bits of stone brought from the top of Baboquivari where Eé toy lives; he held these above Pablo's head as he chanted: "I see the pain. I see the pain. It will go away. It will go away."

Then he reached for his gourd rattle. He whirled this over Pablo's head as he sang four magic songs in a row. Finally he asked Shining Leaf for a cup which he filled with hot water from a pan on the stove. He took some sweet-smelling dry brown leaves from the buckskin bag and put them in this water, stirring them with a small stick, and held the cup to Pablo's lips to drink. Pablo shuddered at the bitter taste, but drained the cup as the shaman had said to do, then he lay back on his blanket.

Now the shaman put all the objects back into his buckskin bag. Finally he carefully lighted his pipe and blew smoke in all four directions, then continued to smoke over Pablo.

Pablo watched him, then fell asleep.

o   o   o

When he awoke it was daylight. Shining Leaf was sitting on the floor beside him. Pablo sat up.

"Where is the medicine man—the shaman—who sat beside me singing?" Pablo's voice was no longer hoarse.

"Blue Eagle smoked beside you until dawn. Now you are better, but you still need more strength. I will bring you some mush."

Tall Bear came in.

"My grandfather, how did you and Little Badger know where to look for me?"

Tall Bear drew a chair up close, facing Pablo.

"After you did not come home, a coyote wailed and barked outside this village all night, and we heard the cry of another coyote far away in the foothills. Early yesterday morning we saw a rainbow over Baboquivari: one end touched Oidak, the other end touched the earth near the very foothills where we found you later. The coyote still raised his voice outside the village, and the other coyote answered. Many people of Oidak knew that Coyote was trying to help.

"Coyote does not like a great number of people together; so we decided that Little Badger should go along with me in his car to try to find the end of the rainbow where Coyote was crying in the foot-hills. Just outside the village we saw Coyote sitting patiently waiting. When he saw us he lifted his head and gave a long wail. Then he bounded ahead of our car, guiding us through the rough desert.

"When we had gone a long way, another coyote, a lame one, your friend it must have been, joined him. We got out of the car and in a few minutes found you."

Grandfather and grandson exchanged knowing smiles. "We know coyotes travel many, many miles to help a friend—Eé toy gets the message to Coyote when his help is needed. Eé toy also asks the people he has taken to the green fields to help by signaling with the beautiful rainbow."

Pablo said, "I know I should not have left to hunt devil's claw without talking to you and my grandmother. Did Eé toy punish me by giving me the fall and the hurt?"

68

Tall Bear considered. "Not to punish you. To make you think. A leader of people must learn to counsel with others. That way he learns to guide his own actions. Only then can he really lead."

Pablo's eyes were downcast. Had this flaw in his behavior been serious enough to keep him from ever being Governor of the Village and Keeper-of-the-Smoke?

"I did fast and I did suffer, my grandfather. Must I fast and suffer more?"

"You did fast and suffer and you did have a dream, but it was to get something for your own family, not to bring good to all of our people. When you fast and suffer and have a vision that will bring good to all, then, if you are worthy, power will be given to you."

Pablo swallowed, hesitated, then said, "Can you get the devil's claw to my mother? It is tomorrow I go on the bus to the Big School."

His grandfather nodded and laid his hand briefly on Pablo's hand. He seldom did that because after a Papago child is five it is considered improper for parents, especially the father or the grandfather, to demonstrate affection. Pablo knew now that all was right between them.

It gave him courage to ask questions that had

69

plagued him during the summer. "What will it be like at the Big School?" "Will there be electric lights and beds as in the house of my grandfather?" "Will the houses have tin roofs?" "Will the boys ask me to play their games?" "Will they, too, ask questions about my village and whether Tall Bear is really my grandfather?"

Tall Bear, unable to answer, still managed to smile. "Early tomorrow morning the bus will come. Now go to your blanket and sleep well." Then he turned and hurried outside the house before Pablo could ask even one more question.

Pablo walked slowly to his canvas blanket under the mesquite tree. He lay wondering why his grandfather had not answered his questions. Then the answer came; my grandfather did not know because he has never been to the Big School. He sighed, turned over, and was soon asleep.

o   o   o

Long before dawn Pablo heard his grandfather moving inside the house. He also heard sounds from other houses close by.

This was the day the bus would come to take the boys and girls to the Big School. Many would be going for the first time, but they had been told by older brothers and sisters what the big school was like. Pablo, alone, did not have anyone who could tell him.

The morning sun was stealing down the sides of the houses when the bus arrived. All who were going had assembled in front of the village store. Tall Bear, who had walked with Pablo, spoke briefly with the white man in charge. Then he told Pablo, "You are to stand in this line, get on the bus and take a seat. Watch the older boys who have been to the Big School. They will know what to do." He leaned close and spoke low. "There is much to learn. You will listen and work hard." He hesitated, then added, "Two years will be a long time, but if you are busy seeing and learning new things, it will not seem so long." He smiled and gave Pablo's shoulder a pat.

"I will listen and try, my grandfather." Pablo's voice caught. He quickly followed the boy ahead of him up the steps of the bus and slid into a seat.

The driver counted the boys and girls to be sure he had the correct number from this village, then climbed behind the steering wheel. With a blowing of the horn to scatter the village dogs and chickens, they were off to the highway.

at home in Pa Vi

Papago Ramada with
shaish-ki (grass house) in
background

Black fox

Grand father

Haris Hawks attack
a black Tailed jack rabbit

Saquaro fruit harvest

On to Oidak

Papago Basket Maker
and devil's claw

In The fields

Baboquivari Peak

Trailing the devil's claw

the storm

School World

1. The Big School

All day they drove. All day Pablo sat watching out the window at the changing countryside. It was late afternoon when they reached the city where the Big School was. Buildings clustered together. Everything was strange. So many cars rushing past. So many people hurrying along. Pablo's eyes hurt with the unfamiliar movement. His ears ached to the roar of sounds blasting through the open windows of the bus.

The bus turned off a wide, busy street and into a tree-lined driveway. The older boys and girls began to chatter and laugh. When the bus stopped they stood in the aisle, impatient to get out.

Pablo sat still, his hands nervously clutching a small canvas bag that held his few belongings. They had stopped in front of a tall, square, frame building—one of a group that had served as school and home for Indian children for almost seventy years. It was a two-story building with lots of glass windows in its walls.

The bus driver spoke some words in English, but his gestures were clear. Pablo saw he must leave the protection of the bus. He got up stiffly and followed the others.

Outside, he found himself in a soft green world —an amazing world. Grass for miles, or so it seemed to him, and all of it green. Trees so tall they rubbed the sky itself. Flowers of many bright colors, and—wonder of wonders—water running in a whirling stream on the grass.

An older Papago boy, one he had never seen before, came down the walk and spoke to him in Papago. "Come with me," he said abruptly, almost rudely. "I am your supervisor."

Pablo was shocked. Could Black Fox have been right? Did Papago boys forget their manners when they came to the Big School?

Pablo followed the boy up the steps of the frame building. As they reached the porch, the big door swung open. He saw a long line of boys, all dressed alike in blue denim, march past. Pablo and the older boy went inside. A darting look and

Pablo saw a long bench. On it were the smaller boys and girls who had come with him on the bus.

"Stay here," the older boy said. Pablo sat down at the end of the line, his canvas bag on his lap.

A heavy door at the left opened, and a small, gray-haired white man looked out. He spoke to the older boy in English. The boy nodded and beckoned to the first boy in the line. He took him through the big door and closed it. Those outside waited. Each time the door opened, a boy next in line was motioned to enter. Girls were directed, by an older girl, to a door on the right side of the room. Not one of the boys or girls came back. Finally it was Pablo's turn.

He tried to walk tall. He tried to think, I am an Indian. I am a Papago. I am not afraid. But he gripped hard on the bag he held.

The white man was sitting at a desk. The older boy was standing beside him.

The white man spoke to Pablo in English, then the older boy said, "He says, 'what is your name?' "

Pablo stood silent, thinking. Papago people did not say names glibly. How could one of the desert people be so impolite as to ask?

The white man tapped his pencil.

"Older Son," Pablo whispered doubtfully.

85

The older boy shook his head impatiently. "That won't do here. Too many older sons."

"Pablo," he answered. He thought his problem was solved.

But the white man asked another question. The older boy translated. "What do people call your father?"

This was agony for Pablo. To have to say his father's name to a strange white man. He kept silent.

The white man, bothered, frowned and spoke sharply to Older Boy. Pablo did not understand, but he didn't want to cause Older Boy any trouble. He whispered, "Red Deer."

The white man wrote, "Pablo Red Deer."

"What is his age?"

The older boy looked at Pablo and guessed aloud, "Twelve."

Pablo understood some numbers in English. He had heard them during the summer at Oidak. He started to say eleven. But it would be impolite to dispute Older Boy. So Pablo was enrolled—"Pablo Red Deer—Age 12."

Older Boy opened a door at the far side of the room. Pablo followed him down the hall to a high-ceilinged room.

The Big School

Here was a new man in a white coat. There was a line of boys, and a lady dressed in white.

"This is the white medicine man," Older Boy said. "He is called a doctor. The lady is a nurse. Do what they tell you. If you don't understand, watch the older boys here and do as they do."

Pablo watched the boy ahead of him. In his turn he stepped forward. The doctor took hold of his shoulder, moved him to a better light. Pablo flinched. But if he had to go through this to learn the magic of the white man, he could do it.

The doctor signaled him to undress to join several naked boys waiting to step, one after the other, under a jet of steaming water to soap their heads and bodies. This all seemed shameful; among his people baths were ceremonials prepared for with fasting and prayers to Great Spirit. This was also a sinful waste of water.

After the shower each boy took a towel from a stack, dried himself, and carried his belongings into an adjoining room. There a short, kind-faced man measured each boy with his eyes, handed him underwear, blue denim trousers, shirt, and jacket, a pair of socks and black shoes.

"Lots of new clothes," the man spoke quietly in Papago to Pablo.

Pablo looked up quickly, hesitated, then whispered wistfully, "Will I see you again?"

The man nodded. "I'll be around. I work here. They call me Frank."

Pablo had never worn shoes. It took a little time to get them on. He stood up cautiously and tried a step or two. His feet felt very heavy. He saw Older Boy enter the room again and walk slowly toward him. Older Boy looked at him with a wry smile and pointed to the shoes. "You'll get used to them—after a while." He added under his breath, "Like a lot of other things here. I'll take you to the dormitory where you'll live. Come along."

As they walked, Older Boy said: "Don't ever pick flowers. Don't make marks on the wall or in your books. Always be careful about touching anything. Everything belongs to the white man's government—even you and I," he added bitterly.

Pablo did not get the meaning of these words, but he did understand that, for some reason, he must not touch flowers here as he had been free to do at home.

They entered a big frame building very much like the other. Older Boy led the way into a large room filled with double-deck narrow beds. Other boys of Pablo's size were coming in.

88

"Put your bag in this cupboard; it is where you will keep things that belong to you." Older Boy pointed. He indicated one of the lower bunks. "This is where you will sleep. Now you're on your own."

Pablo looked around cautiously, then sat down on the edge of his bed. He carefully shifted his weight. The bed did not wiggle like the one in his grandfather's house. He was glad of that. What should he do now? He did not know, so he sat and waited. He knew how to wait.

The loud shrill of a bell made Pablo jump. The other boys began leaving the room so he got up and followed. He was to learn that now his life would be directed by bells.

Timidly he joined the line of boys going along the board walk. The line turned and went through the doors of another building. Inside was a dining room. Each boy slid into a place on a bench at a long table. Pablo found himself sandwiched between the boy who had been just ahead of him in the line and the one who had walked behind; neither one was a Papago. He did not like the closeness of eating this way, but he was hungry and he was glad his grandparents had taught him to eat at a table with a knife and fork.

There was some chatter, but he sat in silence.

"You have to speak English. No Indian here is permitted to speak his own language, so the sooner you learn English, the easier it will be for you," Older Boy had said.

When the meal ended the others stood up. He stood up. They formed a line. He got in place. They marched back to the dormitory. He was with them. In the dormitory he kept watching and imitating. He was beginning to learn.

After he crawled into bed—when the others did —he lay wide awake. The room was stuffy with the smell of boys' bodies. Pablo longed to go out where the green grass was. In his bed he could not hear any of the hushed outdoor night sounds, only the deep breathing of other boys and occasional coughing from the bed above him.

Sleep would not come. He remembered Oidak and Pa Vi. On the desert, the air felt clear and good at night. He recalled Black Fox as he stretched out an arm and swept it toward the sunset, saying, "Great Spirit has given us a beautiful land."

He thought of his mother stirring a pot of beans over the cook-fire in the ramada and a pan of tortillas standing on the stone hearth ready to eat. He remembered one night when his father had hummed a song and, while Younger Brother clapped his hands to the tune, danced around the ramada holding the hands of Younger Sister. He remembered taking one of Younger Sister's hands. The three of them had danced together, and Black Fox had stood at the ramada entrance smiling.

2. Hopi Language

At first it wasn't easy for Pablo to talk to other boys. Except for the Papagos, Pablo couldn't understand them. They were all from different tribes and spoke their own languages.

Learning to say strange-sounding words the teacher put on the blackboard or pointed to under pictures in a book was particularly hard for Pablo, because English had not been taught him at Pa Vi. His teachers were often impatient, lacking understanding and sympathy for tongues and cultures other than that of the white man.

But it was fun to copy curly marks the teacher put on the board and called "writing," or to put little sticks and rocks in clusters to match the "numbers" the teacher called out, counting, adding, taking away, as fast as she asked. Soon he could do this faster than the others. Then he could sit while the teacher helped the other children—his mind filled with ideas far away.

One day after the teacher asked him to count the children in his class and he had counted thirty-eight. Then he asked her, "Will you please tell me how many children in this whole school?"

After a minute she said, "About 400, Pablo. That is more than you can count now."

"I'll learn." Pablo answered quietly. Then he asked another question.

"Will you please tell me how many teachers?"

"Fourteen," she answered quickly, then Pablo heard her say softly, "Not half enough."

This was a curious world he was living in, he thought. No rain-making ceremonies, yet there was lots of water—did these fourteen teachers have some kind of power? How had it come to them?

o   o   o

Pablo soon discovered a new ally in a Hopi boy named Ralph. Ralph had been assigned to work with him on a dishwashing job. He was about a year older than Pablo but he, too, was a beginner in English. Neither boy knew the language of the other. At first, during their work, they could only converse through gestures and smiles. But when they had learned some English they made a game of trying to learn the English names of things used in the kitchen.

Ralph was very easy to get along with—the result of having played with many boys and girls in his own and other Hopi villages. Working with Ralph through the fall and winter, Pablo gradually lost some of his shyness.

One day not long after they had begun working together, Ralph pointed to a pot of beans.

"What do you call these?"

"Beans," said Pablo in his best English.

"No, what do you call them in Papago?"

Pablo looked quickly around to make sure no one was near enough to hear him say an Indian word. "*Pah-vo*," he replied.

Ralph chuckled. "We Hopis call beans '*mo'ri*,' but we have different names for different kinds."

Pablo understood. He asked, "What do you call field?"

"*Pa'sa*," whispered Ralph.

"We say '*auyt*.' "

"Bird?" asked Ralph.

"*Uwhik*," said Pablo.

"*Ci'ro,*" from Ralph.

They had been watching each other closely. Not only were the words different, but each boy, in pronouncing them, had a different way of placing his teeth and tongue. Their breaths sounded different too, when they inhaled or exhaled in making words.

"Hard to learn your language, I'll bet," Ralph said with a grin.

"Yours too," said Pablo. "Maybe it's good we learn English. And we don't have to whisper that."

Before many months, by patient and constant effort, Ralph and Pablo both mastered enough English to move into a class with boys near their own recorded age. When this happened Pablo found his homesickness lessening.

o   o   o

One Saturday morning in early May, when the smell of blossoming bushes and newmown lawn filled the crisp air, Pablo stopped Ralph on their way to the dormitory. He flung himself down on the grass near a huge saguaro growing beside the walk, and Ralph dropped down too.

"Look up there," said Pablo.

Ralph looked. On the very crests of the saguaro's three upthrust arms were clusters of white blossoms touched with gold. A big white-winged gray dove was busily pecking at one cluster.

"Pretty," said Ralph. "What kind of bird is it?"

"I don't know its name. I was thinking that after awhile those blossoms will turn into red fruit filled with sweet juice. We pick and eat the fruit—do Hopis like it?"

"We don't have saguaros on the Hopi reservation," Ralph said.

"Well, we'll never get a taste of the fruit from this saguaro." Pablo mimicked: " 'Belongs to the guv-ment.' "

Both boys laughed.

They fell silent. Then Ralph said softly, as if he'd been thinking about it a long time: "I have another name—an Indian name. Have you?" Pablo nodded.

Ralph continued. "My name is Honhoya—in English it means Little Bear. What's your name?"

"I'm not supposed to say it. The medicine man gave it to me to keep but not to say. All our people have names they don't say because using a name the medicine man gives may wear it out." He waited, fearing to hurt Ralph's feelings, but unable to speak his sacred name.

After a minute Ralph said, "What the medicine man says you must obey."

Pablo, happy at this reply, quickly asked, "What is the name of your village?"

"Walpi. What's yours?"

"Pa Vi." Then Pablo asked, "How far is your village from here?"

"A long, long way—almost two days to get to my village in an automobile—even longer to get to some of our other villages."

"How many villages have you?"

"All together, twelve. Nine are built on three mesa tops, two at the foot of mesas, and one outside the reservation in the valley, where the people have their gardens near their homes."

"What is a—mesa? Is it like a hill?"

"Yes, like a hill, but it is higher, and flatter on top. It is a long way down from the top where we live to the rocks below, about 300 feet down. We go on trails that switch back and forth because it is so steep. Now tell me about your villages."

Pablo wondered if it would seem like bragging to have so many more villages than Ralph's people had. Finally he said, "Our villages are far away too.

We have about seventy, I think, but some have only about twenty people living in them. A few others have as many as three hundred. My grandfather's village of Oidak has about two hundred people, but Pa Vi has only thirty-five.

"Pa Vi is sheltered in the mountains, quiet and away from roads, but we have to go a long way— five or six miles—with barrels in a wagon to get water from a spring for drinking, cooking, and washing. We don't have enough water for fields or gardens, or enough room either. So each summer we go to our camp on the desert, where we plant beans and corn and stay until we harvest the crops. On the desert we build ponds that we call *charcos*, to hold crop water when the rains come.

"Each year when we go to summer camp we watch the saguaros growing near our fields. The blossoms, like those up there, turn to fruits. Then when the leader of our village tells us they are ripe enough, we pick them with long sticks. The first ones we pick, we eat pulp and juice and throw the shells down red-side up so rain will come. After that everyone fills baskets and jars with fruits so the ladies can cook the pulp and juice and make syrup. They put this syrup in big ollas to ferment.

"The medicine man decides when the juice is

ready to drink and when the clouds are right; then he says it is time to begin the cactus festival to ask Eé toy, Great Spirit, for rain. That night a place is smoothed for dancing and a giant fire is lighted in the center of it, then all the people form a ring around the fire, clasp hands and dance until first dawn. All the men and ladies have been drinking the cactus syrup so their bodies will be moist, clean, and strong as the earth becomes when it rains. The old men sing rain songs. This is the beginning of the New Year, and all are very happy because they are getting evil feelings out of their minds. They keep drinking cactus syrup as long as it lasts, and praying to Great Spirit for rain.

"Sometimes the rain comes fast—maybe even during the prayers—and we lift our faces to feel cool water on our skin. If lots of rain comes we have to work hard in the gardens to keep the water from washing away our plants. There is mud everywhere and we slip and slide around, but we are all happy and it is fun."

Pablo stopped, and looked to see if Ralph was going to make fun of this.

But Ralph seemed very much interested. "So that's the way your people make rain," he said. "In my country we have a rain dance with snakes."

"Snakes?" Pablo shivered a little. "I don't know about getting rain that way. Tell about it."

"Well, in my country," Ralph began, "we have a dance for rain every August. It is held in Walpi one year, in one of the other villages the next, then in Walpi the next year, and so on."

Pablo asked, "What happens to Walpi's crops the years the dance is held somewhere else?"

"Oh, the dancers always ask the Rain God to give rain for the crops of all our villages. Our snake brothers are the messengers to the Gods underground who bring rain, and our dance is to keep the snakes in good humor.

"Among the Hopis we have a Snake Clan, which has charge of the ceremony. Each day for four days—one day for each direction, north, south, east, west—Snake priests go out into the desert and bring back snakes of every kind they can find, rattlers, bull snakes, and others. They keep them in the village kiva for eight days washing and sprinkling them with cornmeal in secret ceremonials.

"Priests from the Antelope Clan always help because long, long ago Snake priests cured an Antelope person who was bitten by a snake.

"On the ninth day we have the snake dance.

Just before the sun goes down, the Antelope priests come marching out of the kiva singing. They wear shell and turquoise necklaces, and white buckskin kilts, and each has a foxskin tied to his waist in back to look like a tail. Each one also has a turtle-shell rattle fastened to the back of his right knee, and he carries two gourd rattles to keep time in the dance. All the Antelope priests have black-and-white zigzag stripes painted on their chests and arms, like streaks of lightning. They march to one side of the plaza and wait there in a line."

Ralph sat and hugged his knees, his eyes shining. "Now come the Snake priests out of the kiva. They too are wearing necklaces and foxskin tails, but their deerskin kilts are brown and they wear bunches of feathers in their hair. Their faces are blackened and their mouths painted white, and the lower parts of their legs and arms are painted pink.

"They dance around the plaza three times to the songs of the Antelope priests. Then they stoop over the *kisi*, a bower made of cottonwood branches, where one of the Snake priests is now guarding all the snakes. As each Snake priest stands up straight again he is holding in his mouth a wriggling snake."

Pablo, listening raptly, made a wry face. "No

one could hold a live rattlesnake in his mouth," he said. "It would bite him."

Ralph said, "Snakes don't bite the Snake priests because the priests have good hearts and pray for rain for all the people."

He continued. "Well, the Snake priests dance around the plaza with the snakes in their mouths, while the Antelope priests keep singing. Every snake in the *kisi* gets danced around the plaza four times in its turn; then it is dropped to the ground and a gatherer picks it up.

"Finally all the snakes are tossed into a circle on the ground, where a cornmeal design has been made. After a few minutes the Snake priests grab handfuls of them and run down the trails away from the village to take them back to their desert homes, so they can get word to the God who brings rain."

"Does rain always come?" Pablo asked, a little doubtfully.

"Most always it comes very soon, lots of it." Now Ralph giggled. "I am just thinking about the white tourists who come to our village to see this dance. They poke their heads into our houses and ask rough questions, and make big laughs, but most always on their way home they get caught in a bad storm and some of their cars get stuck in the mud. This is the way our Gods get even with them for being so rude."

"Do many white people visit your village?" Pablo asked in some surprise.

"Oh yes, too many—and I can tell you some funny stories. When lots of white Americans come to see our snake dance, they crowd our village and they get close to the edge of the cliffs. They keep yelling at each other not to fall off. My Uncle Joe speaks very good English, and one day a white lady said to him, 'Don't your people often fall off this cliff?' Uncle Joe did not smile but he said, 'Not often, only once.' Then this lady tells her husband, 'This man says only once has anyone fallen off this cliff.'" Both boys rolled on the grass laughing.

"Another time," Ralph said, "one of the rude white ladies asked my uncle, 'Why do you wear red bands around your heads?' He said, 'Come over here and I'll whisper a secret to you.' She followed him a little way, and my uncle whispered, 'Don't ever tell anybody—but we all wear wigs, and this red band holds them on our heads.' The white lady looked surprised and promised she would never tell."

3. He-Who-Runs-Far

At the Big School on Saturday afternoons during the school year, there were games. Ralph often took part in the games, but Pablo was usually at the outer edge of the group.

One night while Pablo and Ralph were washing dishes, Ralph said, "On Saturday I'm going to run in a relay race, but one of the boys on my team is sick. Will you take his place? I know you can run fast. I have seen you run from one building to another."

At first Pablo couldn't believe that he was actually being invited to be one of a team. He hid his feelings and accepted. "I will run with you."

Ralph's eyes sparkled. "I will be the third runner on our team and you will be the fourth. I will be running against a Navajo boy and you against an

Apache boy on the other team. I will try to get far ahead of the Navajo boy so you will have a head start on the Apache. Grab my stick fast when I hand it to you, and run hard so the Apache boy can't catch up with you. Each day after class we'll practice so you'll know just how to grab the stick and not drop it."

On Friday night before the race, Pablo lay awake. What if the team should lose because of him? What if he could not run fast enough? What if he should drop the stick? He pushed away these painful thoughts, trying to sleep. Then it seemed he saw on the windowsill, close to his bed, a coyote sitting quietly on its haunches. Pablo sat up, slid out of bed and hurried toward the sill. Coyote disappeared from the window.

"Coyote!" Pablo whispered. "Coyote, wait! It's me, Pablo."

He looked out into the bright moonlight. Across the lawn, near the trees, was a shadowy gray form, traveling through the shrubs as fast as it could with a limping left front foot, and Pablo thought a quiet voice whispered his ceremonial name, "HE-WHO-RUNS-FAR."

In the morning he tried to remember how he got back to his bed after Coyote's visit. He couldn't remember at all. "Anyhow, I'm sure I heard my ceremonial name," he decided. "Today I must be worthy of my name."

The afternoon was bright and sunny. Most of the school's boys, and girls too, came to watch the games. Pablo, with Ralph, watched closely, joining in cheers for the winners, until time came for the relay races. When their race was called, Pablo found himself excited but not frightened. The two teams lined up.

"Ready, get set—Go!" yelled the gym teacher, and the first runner on each team left the starting place together.

The boys on the two teams matched very well, the first one a little ahead, then the other, until Ralph's turn came. He forged steadily ahead after half the distance was covered. When he neared the spot where Pablo was waiting, hand out-stretched, Ralph was about six long steps ahead of the Navajo. Hardly slackening his speed, he handed the stick to Pablo, who was already running. Pablo took it from him smoothly and was off on his turn. He had the stick safely and felt sure he could keep ahead.

But he did not know the speed of the Apache boy, who by now had the other stick from the

Navajo. Soon he heard the *pit, pit, pit* of running feet gaining on him. Out of the corner of his eye he saw a flash of blue. The Apache boy, in the blue shirt, was passing him.

"Run," he thought he heard Coyote's voice calling. "Run, He-Who-Runs-Far. Run!"

Strength poured into his flying legs. He flung himself forward to overtake the Apache. He passed him just at the finish line.

The close race brought cheers from the watching boys and girls. As Pablo slowed to a stop, his running mates crowded around him, laughing and shouting, "We did it! We won it!" Ralph ran up and gave him a bear hug.

After that day Pablo became a part of a group. One boy after another showed that they liked him. Now there was always someone near to laugh and exchange little jokes with him. He quickly came to know boys from other Indian reservations —Navajo, Paiute, Apache, Mohave. In the schoolroom he scanned a map of Arizona and adjoining states to place the home spots of each boy he met.

Mr. Cole, the gym teacher, had told him right after the race, "Pablo, you can be a good track man. Just stay with it and soon you will be able to run faster than any boy in this school."

Pablo was surprised and pleased. From then on, in his every spare moment, he put on his trunks and running shoes and went to the recreation field to practice. Now Mr. Cole entered him in the 50- and 100-yard dashes in addition to relay races. Steadily, with a few good instructions, he found he could increase his speed. Before the end of the school year there was no doubt: Pablo was the fastest runner in his age group.

One morning just before school was out, Mr. Cole was waiting for Pablo when he came from a practice run. He put his hand on Pablo's shoulder and said, "Pablo, next year I am going to enter you in races with boys from three other Indian schools. I have talked with gym teachers in these places and we think some competition between the schools would be good. I am sure you will be able to win your races and our school will be very proud of you. Just keep practicing through the summer, and next year we'll show them a real runner." Pablo looked up at Mr. Cole, swallowed and nodded. The teacher smiled at him and walked on.

"He-Who-Runs-Far," Pablo whispered softly. "Thank you, Brother Coyote. I'll try very hard."

But his high hopes were swiftly dashed.

4. White Man's Machine

The very next Sunday morning as Pablo was crossing the school yard, he came upon the white supervisor of grounds, Mr. Werner, working noisily to start the gasoline motor of the tractor-mower he rode in cutting the lawns. Mr. Werner tugged again and again at the starter cord, in vain; he reached for the small can of kerosene he used to prime the motor and saw that he had set it down on the ground near where Pablo stood watching.

"Bring that can!" he commanded. Pablo looked around, decided the man was speaking to him and got the small can he saw under the tree.

Mr. Werner grabbed the can from Pablo's hands, tipped it up, shook it. "This can's almost empty," he growled.

He tried a few more quick pulls of the cord

to get the motor started, but nothing happened. Then, angry and red-faced, he shouted at Pablo, "Here, you! Take this can to the shop and get it filled. Well, don't stand there. Run!" Then he said, loud enough for Pablo to hear, "Dumb Indians. Too bad they weren't all scalped. All of 'em dirty, lousy, lazy."

Pablo stood a minute disbelieving he had heard such words. Then he stooped and picked up the can to obey. Behind him he heard the motor start suddenly. Turning to look, he heard Werner yell, "Get out of the way, dummy!" But before Pablo could move, the oncoming machine struck his right leg. Pablo twisted to get out of the way, hit the ground and rolled.

When he tried to get up he found the pain in his right leg too great. The white supervisor, having stopped the mower, was standing over him. "Don't play possum with me, kid," he said. "Get up."

Pablo tried hard to rise, but couldn't. He saw, to his relief, that Mr. Cole, the gym teacher, had come upon the scene.

"What's the matter, Pablo?" Mr. Cole asked.

"I hurt my leg," Pablo answered without looking at Werner.

White Man's Machine

The gym teacher put an arm under Pablo's shoulders to help him stand, but Pablo could not bear his weight on his right leg.

"How did this happen?" Harry Cole turned angrily to the supervisor.

"Dumb kid couldn't get out of the way of the mowing machine. I yelled at him when I saw him standing right in the way. If I hadn't stopped the mower fast, he'd have been hurt worse. These stupid Indian kids don't know anything about machinery and they can't or won't learn. If they don't know, they figure they won't have to work." Pablo, held up by the gym teacher, looked hard into Werner's eyes, but did not speak.

"I'll help you to the infirmary, Pablo," Harry Cole said. "We'll have the doctor take a look at that leg." Turning to Werner he said, "Don't forget to report this accident to the superintendent—or shall I do it?"

"That's up to me," snapped Werner.

At the infirmary the doctor looked carefully at Pablo's leg and said to Cole, "Looks like a pulled ligament to me. How serious I'll know better after I see the X-rays." He turned to Pablo. "How did this happen?"

Pablo said only, "I got in the way of the

mower." The doctor and Mr. Cole exchanged glances.

The doctor said, "Well, he'll have to stay off that leg for a while. Must have had his feet solidly on the ground when he was hit, and twisted his knee as he fell."

After X-rays and bandaging, Mr. Cole asked, "Pablo, how did this really happen?"

Pablo hesitated—"The supervisor told you."

"Not all white men are like Werner," Mr. Cole said firmly. "Remember, many white Americans respect and honor your people."

Pablo nodded, gave a little smile.

5. When Will the Buses Go?

As Pablo lay in an infirmary bed recovering, he thought about Pa Vi, about Oidak and his people. He remembered how the medicine man at Oidak had treated him; he wished he were here now to treat the injured leg. Then an exciting idea came. It was the end of his first year; some boys and girls were going back to their reservations. He had heard them planning for it. Why shouldn't he ride the bus back to Oidak with the others returning there? He might get the medicine man to cure his leg; he could work with his grandfather during the summer; maybe, with luck, Little Badger could take him for a visit to Pa Vi. At the end of the summer he could come back on the bus for his second school year.

When Mr. Cole came in later to see him, Pablo

said, "I think I'd like to go to my grandfather's home this summer. When will the buses go?"

Mr. Cole hesitated, then said, "Pablo, the school does not send boys and girls back to their reservations until they have been here at least two years. Didn't your grandfather know that?"

"He said I would be in the Big School two years, but why couldn't I go back to Oidak and come back with the others in the bus next fall?" His eyes looked straight into those of Mr. Cole.

"I will try to explain, Pablo. The teachers here work very hard to teach new boys and girls English and other useful things. Things like eating correctly, taking baths and keeping the head clean, wearing freshly washed clothes each week. These things may be hard for boys and girls to do on their reservations, so they go back to their old ways of living, and they forget much of their English because their people do not speak English very well, if at all. Children come back to school in the fall, many with bad colds, dirty clothes, bodies, and heads, and much less English than when they left. It seems better to keep the boys and girls here away from their reservations for at least two years. Some who stay longer than two years don't go home or see their families until they graduate from the tenth grade—maybe five or six years after the time they came."

Pablo had listened carefully. "This is the orders of the school?"

"Yes, Pablo. Do you understand?"

Pablo sighed. "Yes, I understand I can't go, but I still wish I could." He turned his face to the wall. Mr. Cole laid a gentle hand on Pablo's shoulder and, without speaking again, left the room.

o   o   o

The pangs of loneliness Pablo had felt when he started at the Big School he felt again, to some extent, at the beginning of summer vacation. Many of the boys and girls who had been at the school two or more years went back to their reservations, including some of his newly made friends, and in nearly every case this meant he would not see them ever again. Next fall there would be new Indian boys and girls in their places.

About 240 girls and boys remained at the school during the summer. There were no classes to attend, but there was no real vacation, either. Only two teachers stayed through the hot months, and they worked with the administrative staff supervising the boys and girls on different jobs. There was plenty of work to keep everyone busy.

Besides his dishwashing, Pablo found himself doing many chores needed at a boarding school to get it ready for a fresh start. Someone had to wash the inside walls of the dormitories and dining room; sand and wax floors; scrub, repair and paint lockers, tables and chairs; count and mend towels, sheets, and various kinds of books that would be used in classes; keep showers and toilets in operating order. In time Pablo shared in most of these jobs, although his leg remained stiff.

Because there were fewer dishes to wash, Ralph had been taken off this detail for the summer and put to work with men building a new adobe barn. Pablo seldom saw Ralph after classes ended.

The boys and girls were kept busy all day through each week until Saturday noon; then the afternoon was given over to baths and head washings. Pablo found that he missed the Saturday afternoon games and races very much; even if he couldn't have run in them, he could have watched.

Sunday forenoon there was chapel, and all were required to attend; but after the Sunday midday meal there was the only chance of the whole week for any social activity—three hours of free time when boys and girls could wander about the grounds, or sit and talk together while some adult kept an eye on them.

Pablo found that he disliked the restraint and drab monotony even more than he had disliked, at first, the noise and rushing about.

During the week, as his work took him from building to building, he tried to run a little to get a sense of freedom and to limber his injured leg. And on Sunday afternoons he used much of his free time to run on the track to improve the leg, but he found himself running alone.

o   o   o

Occasionally he crossed the grounds to the printing shop, where he had found that Frank, the Papago man, worked. Sometimes he would slip into the shop, watch Frank at work, get a nod and a smile, and wait quietly. Frank, when he had finished his task, would say, "Now we can sit on the steps and get some fresh air." They would talk or just sit in companionable silence.

One time as he sat on the steps of the printing shop with Frank he asked, "Have you been here a long time?"

"Eight years. Why do you ask?"

"Have you learned this thing called magic of the white man? I haven't. I'm not sure now that I even know what it is. I can't go back until I know, so I can help our people."

Frank answered thoughtfully. "You have learned to speak and read and write English pretty well. That is part of the magic you were sent to learn. I think the other part of the magic is learning the skills of the white man and the way he has developed them."

"Is that what you learn here in this shop? Could you teach our people the job you're doing here now?"

Frank studied about this before he answered. "I have learned to set type and follow the copy my boss gives me. There wouldn't be any use for this kind of work on our reservation because we don't have a written language, and almost none of our people read English."

"Then you will always have to work here under a white boss, or someplace in the world of the white man?" Pablo's eyes searched Frank's face for the answer.

"I don't know. Some days I think about going back, but mostly I think about trying to get a job in a white man's shop." He paused. "But now I just work and try to learn more here." He touched Pablo lightly on the elbow. "I must get back to work now."

Pablo rose reluctantly. "I think I can never learn enough to be Governor of the village and Keeper-of-the-Smoke, as my grandfather wishes," he said sadly. "Maybe I can't go back, ever."

Frank stopped. "You'll go back. You will always belong on the desert. When it calls, you will answer."

He turned to go into the shop. But Pablo, full of unanswered questions, put his hand out to detain him. Frank took a step toward the shop, looked inside, hesitated, then resolutely turned back and sat down.

"Here they have water," Pablo began. "The rain falls, but I do not think they sing for it. I have not seen a rain-making ceremony. If they can get rain without singing for it, what about their visions and dreams? Does the Unknown give them rain and water to use so carelessly without singing and praying for it? Is this the magic I must learn?" The boy's earnestness demanded an answer.

Frank sighed. "Pablo, our people have always

lived in a land where there is little water. They love the land they live on and they treasure the water because it is scarce."

Pablo pondered this a minute. "In our village," he said, "water must be hauled in barrels in a wagon from a well six miles away."

Frank nodded understandingly. "Some white people have found magic to get water to dry land by wells and dams and canals. Some Indians did this too in the olden days. Coyotes have a way to get water, too."

Pablo looked up. "How do they know?"

"I don't know, but Eé toy has given Coyote this power. Coyotes will dig down three or four feet in the dry desert country, not straight down, but slanting holes, to get water. These holes are so small a person has to dip water out with a little can, and the water isn't very good or clear, but it keeps life in a man or an animal.

"Sometime Eé toy will give this power to some of our Papagos. Then our land will have water for all our people."

Pablo turned to look squarely at Frank. "You think sometime one of our people will be shown how to get more water on our land?" His heart jumped.

"Yes, I believe that," Frank said simply.

During Pablo's second year at the school he tried practice runs on the track alone or with Ralph. He found he could not keep up with Ralph since the accident to his leg. But Ralph and some of the other boys came to consult him. "How did I do today, Pablo?" or "Any ideas about how I can speed up?" And Pablo discovered he could help them—especially with advice on breathing for the longer races.

Mr. Cole, the gym teacher, was quick to notice this. He assured Pablo, "Even if you can't make the team again, Pablo, you can help the boys win track meets."

Pablo went to watch the other boys practice and to see them run. He stayed on the sidelines and cheered, wishing very much he could be running with them.

But this year, some way, bit by bit, Pablo began to lose the warmth of excitement he had felt about learning the magic of the white man. He was as anxious as ever to please his grandfather, so he kept doggedly working to learn English and the other things the white teachers taught—arithmetic, reading, and geography. But sometimes he wondered whether these were actually things his grandfather thought would teach him the magic of the white man.

o   o   o

As Pablo neared the end of his second year, the time his grandfather expected him back, he was greatly troubled. He felt that he could speak English quite well, but his grandfather had hoped for more than that. He had counted on Pablo to bring real knowledge to help their people on the reservation. Pablo had decided "magic" meant skills, but he hadn't learned any skills really. Could the fault be in him?

Maybe if he stayed just one more year and could be assigned to work out-of-doors with the men in charge of growing shrubs and plants, then he would be able to tell his grandfather things about irrigating and fertilizing that would help their people. He thought about this a long time. He wanted to go home—but the wish was not as strong as it had been last year.

He tried to look into his own feelings to find what he should do. What he found disturbed him. Looking back, he recalled that when Ralph and other boys first had told him about their tribal customs and beliefs, he simply thought them wrong when they differed from Papago beliefs. But he had found that the boys were as loyal to their traditions as he was to his. Maybe their tribes are as right as mine, he admitted to himself. But he did not like to think that any of his own traditions might be wrong. He took long walks to fight such thoughts.

Then he had a further disturbing thought: although he felt he wasn't yet learning the white man's skills, was he learning to like the white man's way of living better than the way of his people?

He knew he should return home at the end of this second year, but he was ashamed to go back and say to Tall Bear and to Red Deer, "I didn't learn anything that will help our people. I know only things that will help me if I stay in the land of the white man."

Finally he decided he had to talk with Mr. Cole about staying on another year. Mr. Cole was pleased with the idea. He said, "I think Mr. Parker might arrange to let you work with the supervisors of the grounds and the gardens next year. Let's go talk with him about it."

After Pablo told Mr. Parker his wish, the two men asked him to wait on the porch a minute while they talked it over. Through the open window Pablo heard the voice of Mr. Cole. "This boy is brighter than many of the others. He is eager to learn, and works hard at any task given to him. We shouldn't let him go back to the reservation now and lose all he has gained here. This boy should stay on at the school and graduate from the tenth grade."

Then Mr. Parker's voice. "The first year he was here he seemed more eager and alert and did better work in the classroom than he has this year. That year he was our fastest runner among the younger boys, wasn't he?"

Mr. Cole answered, "Yes. He had every chance of being a fine track man—before that accident to his leg."

There was a silence. Then Mr. Parker spoke slowly: "Yes, I remember that accident. Well, it's all right with me to keep him another year, or even until he graduates, if he does good work. I certainly don't want to see a bright boy go back to be a blanket Indian on a reservation. I'll put him on yard work with one of the supervisors who'll teach him how to grow things, if that's the way you want it."

He added, with a laugh, "If he doesn't make the grade, I'll hold you responsible."

Mr. Cole's reply was pleasant. "I'll take that chance." Then he said, "We'll have to let his grandfather know, won't we?"

"I'll tell the bus driver to tell the old man, if he sees him."

Then Mr. Parker called Pablo in and said, "We have decided to assign you to work on the school grounds and in the gardens if you want to stay another year. Maybe you will decide you'd like to stay until you graduate—and if your work is good and you obey your teachers and the yard supervisor, we would let you do that—maybe."

The plan for next year sounded good to Pablo. "Thank you Mr. Parker," he said. Then to Mr. Cole, "And thank you, too. I wish I could run on your track team again, but my leg is still not good enough."

"You have helped the team many times, Pablo, by your advice and interest. You really give them lots of encouragement. That's one of the best ways you can help the school win."

Pablo now hurried to find Ricardo Wells, an older boy from Oidak who he knew was returning to that village. "Ricardo, will you tell my grandfather I am staying another year so I can learn more?"

Ricardo narrowed his eyes. "So you are staying on to become a white man."

Pablo ignored Ricardo's tone. "No. Only to learn more to help our people."

Ricardo snorted.

"You'll tell my grandfather?" Pablo persisted.

"Yeh," Ricardo's voice mocked. "I'll tell him."

It was not hard to see Ricardo go. It was harder to see Ralph board a bus and vanish, as Pablo thought, out of his life.

o   o   o

For the boys and girls who stayed at school, this summer was much like last—chores and maintenance work getting the school ready for opening in the fall. Pablo found himself doing the same sort of tasks he had done the previous summer.

One morning in late August, the white lady who worked in Mr. Parker's office called to Pablo as he passed her door.

"Your name is Pablo Red Deer, isn't it?"

Pablo hesitated, then answered softly, "Yes."

She came to the door and held out something. "Here is a letter for you."

Pablo took it slowly from her hand and gazed

at it intently. The first letter he had ever received.

He saw the lady watching him as he read his handwritten name, then studied everything else on the envelope.

"It is from Keams Canyon—the Hopi reservation," she said.

"How do you know?" Pablo said in some suspicion.

"Because of the postmark," she said, and pointed. "The postmark on a letter tells the name of the place where it was mailed."

Pablo thought a moment. "So everyone knows where a letter comes from?"

"That's right."

Pablo nonchalantly stuffed the letter into his jeans pocket and started across the lawn. But he turned back, smiled, and said, "Thank you," while the white lady still watched.

Several times during the morning Pablo took the envelope out of his pocket and read his name, then hurriedly put the letter out of sight. When the bell for noon lunch rang, Pablo ran quickly to the dormitory, where, sitting alone on his bed, he opened the envelope. Inside, on a sheet of tablet paper, was writing. Pablo read: "Hello, Pablo. How are you? I am fine. It is nice to be home. The gardens grow nice. Tomorrow we dance the snakes. Ralph."

Pablo put the letter under his pillow and sat thinking as long as he dared before joining the other boys for lunch.

That night he took out the letter and read it over several times. He made a decision. Tomorrow he would write a letter. He would write to his grandfather. Of course his grandfather couldn't read, but some of the Oidak boys who had been to the Big School could read it to him.

The next day he got a sheet of paper and a pencil from the schoolroom cupboard. On Sunday afternoon in his free time he would write. He hummed softly one of his grandfather's chants.

Sunday afternoon he found a place to sit under some trees where he would not be disturbed, and he started a letter. "Hello, Grandfather." This didn't seem right some way, so he erased the "Hello" and started "My Grandfather." Then he sat a long time thinking before he wrote "How are you? I am fine." He put Ralph's letter away. He couldn't get any more ideas from that.

"How is my grandmother? How are the folks at Pa Vi?" Now ideas came bubbling. "Did my mother get the devil's claw? Did she make baskets with it? Have you seen Coyote with the crippled foot? Are Younger Brother and Sister growing? The grass here is nice. There is much water. I will stay one more year to learn more. I asked Ricardo to tell you. I know you sent me to learn all I can about the white man's skills." He erased "skills" and wrote "magic" instead. Then he signed his name—Pablo. He decided against using the full name the school used—Pablo Red Deer.

He read the letter over—the first letter he had ever written. He felt happy. His grandfather could see he had learned some of the white man's magic. Tomorrow he would ask the lady in the principal's office how to get an envelope and a stamp. He would then write his grandfather's name and Oidak on the envelope and find out how to mail it.

He looked again at Ralph's letter. He knew the stamp and envelope had cost money. He delved in his pocket and brought out twelve pennies. These his grandfather had put in his canvas bag when he left Oidak. Pablo had carefully saved them. There wasn't anything to buy at the Big School—"the gov-ment" furnished everything—even a candy bar now and then for work well done. Now it seemed right to use them to buy a stamp and envelope for a letter to his grandfather.

6. The Buses Come Again

In September when the buses brought their cargoes of new students from reservations, Pablo made sure to be on hand to see the Papago girls and boys alight. Of course there was no one from Pa Vi. But there were the usual number from Oidak, and Pablo hoped some of these might bring a message from his grandfather to say he had received Pablo's letter and approved of Pablo's decision to stay at school this extra year. But no one had a message from Tall Bear. Pablo tried to puzzle out if he should really have expected one.

In parceling out jobs for the new school year, Mr. Parker remembered to assign Pablo to an outdoor detail as promised. This put him under the white supervisor who had taken Mr. Werner's place after the accident. Mr. Tanner was a kindly man who worked hard with his boys, teaching them about fertilizing, watering, and trimming lawns, trees, and shrubs. Pablo liked this man and enjoyed learning about things that seemed more important to him than much of what he was learning in his classroom.

Through the fall months he still thought he might get some word from his grandfather, and when Christmas came and a few boys and girls got colored greeting cards from their reservation families, Pablo shyly looked each day for a card from Oidak with his name on it. But none came.

He shut his jaws together tightly and said to himself, I am really too old to care about such things. But he wondered. Had some of the boys who returned to Oidak told his grandfather that Pablo could not belong to the track team now? He had failed in that. Had they said he hadn't learned anything yet that would help their people? He had failed in that too. These thoughts hung darkly over him. He determined somehow to prove himself by learning everything he could from Mr. Tanner.

o   o   o

At the end of the third year, Pablo again sought

out Mr. Cole. He wished, he said, to stay for one more year to work with the ground and garden supervisor.

"I think that would be a good thing, Pablo. I know that Mr. Tanner would like to have you another year. He spoke to me about it the other day. He said you had a real interest in the work, and he'd like to help you learn more. I hoped you'd decide to stay." Mr. Cole hesitated. "It's all right with your people, isn't it?"

Now it was Pablo's turn to hesitate. Finally he nodded.

"Well, you had better tell Mr. Tanner. I think he wants you to help him this summer with some of the younger boys who are staying on."

For Pablo this was to prove a summer of doing. He found that he enjoyed passing on to the newer boys the things he had learned from Mr. Tanner. And since this was his first summer at the work, he learned from his supervisor the special care that had to be lavished on plants to keep them thriving under the sometimes blistering sun.

o   o   o

When September rolled around again, Pablo once

more watched the buses deliver their loads of new students. Maybe, just maybe, some new boy from Oidak would bring him a message.

Now he received a real shock. Not only was there no message, but the bus from the Papago reservation bore not a single girl or boy from Oidak.

Turning in dismay to some of the older Papago boys arriving from other villages, he asked cautiously in the Papago tongue if they could guess the cause. They said they could not, but several volunteered that there had been great suffering on the Papago reservation because the Great Spirit had sent them no rain, and two of the boys had heard their elders say there had been much trouble about it at Oidak, just what, they didn't know. Pablo walked away thinking of the drought and of the great unhappiness that must be in Oidak and Pa Vi. He knew that Tall Bear and Black Fox, as leaders, must be deeply worried.

7. Season after Season

So Pablo began his fourth year at the school. Because of his good work during the summer with the yard boys, he was assigned to help Mr. Tanner supervise the younger boys on yard and garden duties this fall. He would, of course, be working and learning, too, from Mr. Tanner.

As month followed month he applied himself hard to his classroom work, but his real interest remained with the things outside. Not only did he like teaching the younger boys about ground work while continuing to learn more about it himself, but he was also pleased because he was able to help boys who still kept coming to him for advice on how to improve their running. He began to think that maybe he had a natural bent for teaching others.

Toward the end of the year Pablo analyzed himself again. Could he truly go back to Oidak now and tell his grandfather he had learned the skills of the white man in growing crops? He felt doubtful, but the day before Mr. Tanner had said to him, "Pablo, I'll be glad to have you stay on and work here, but I must tell you I have taught you all I know about garden and yard work. I'm a practical gardener, but you know you have asked me many questions this year that I have been unable to answer. That's because I don't have enough scientific knowledge."

So Pablo decided that now he must go back to the reservation and tell his grandfather the things he had learned, even though they would not come up to Tall Bear's hopes.

He went to tell Mr. Cole his decision. Mr. Cole listened quietly. "Pablo," he said, "I think it would be a big mistake to leave now. You have only one more year here until you can graduate. Whatever you do, on the reservation or off, graduating from this school will help you. Don't run out on a job until you finish it. Graduation is finishing a job."

Pablo frowned. This was a new thought to him. "But the supervisor, Mr. Tanner, said he had taught me all he knew—what would I do?"

"There are still many things you can learn here in the tenth-year classes, even if it isn't about growing crops and getting water for villages. You can learn more about arithmetic, geography, history, better English and grammar, which will help you whatever you do later. Let me talk to Mr. Parker —and you think again about whether you want to run away from a job before completing it."

The next day Mr. Parker, the principal, called Pablo. "Pablo, if you want to stay another year and graduate, I will put you on the dormitory job of supervisor of the younger boys. You worked well with them on yard work. Now you will have full responsibility for the younger boys' dormitory. You will meet them when they arrive from their reservations in the fall, and from then on be responsible for inspection of their personal cleanliness, the way they keep their lockers and dormitory, to see that they speak only English—and there will be other things you will be called on to do for them from time to time.

"Although this is a big job, you will have time to attend your own classes and prepare for graduation next spring. You have shown you can take responsibility and get along well with others. We certainly don't want you to quit now with only one more year until you get your diploma from the tenth grade. Only about six out of every hundred students we get here graduate. Your grandfather will be very proud of you."

The last sentence decided Pablo—if he could make his grandfather proud, then he'd stay. So he began his fifth and last year at the Big School.

8. Blanket Indian

Pablo was now fifteen and strong. The boys in his charge considered him a man. They could not know that he was tormented with worry and doubts about his future. Though he now questioned many of the old ways of his people, he found no satisfying new ways to replace them. Could he now join the white man's world? If so, could he stay an Indian? From what he had heard and seen during these years in school, he had grave doubts that he could get by in the world of the white man. Better go back to his own tribe. Would this please his grandfather? Even though he had been away so long, his people would surely welcome him.

He wished he could talk with Mr. Cole or Frank, but Mr. Cole had left the school in January to take a job in an eastern city school, and Frank had taken a job in the print shop of another Indian school.

About a week before the end of the school year, the principal called Pablo to his office. "Pablo, you're finishing school with good grades. If you want to go to a vocational school and learn a trade, I'll try to get you a scholarship."

Pablo was impressed and pleased by this offer, but he tried not to show emotion as he stood considering it. Finally in a quiet voice he gave his decision. "I must go back to my people. My grandfather has waited a long time."

"What will you do when you get back to the reservation? Not much work there."

"What would I do after I left vocational school?" Pablo asked quietly.

"Why, get a job somewhere. At the vocational school you would learn a trade, maybe as an electrician or a printer. You could get a good job."

"In the world of the white man, Mr. Parker?" In the silence that followed, and under Pablo's direct gaze, the principal flushed. He was annoyed with this boy who questioned too much.

"Of course!" he answered shortly.

Pablo said, "No, I must go back to my people."

Mr. Parker shrugged. Pablo knew he meant "What good has school done this boy? He'll go back to the reservation and be a blanket Indian."

Pablo then asked a question he had had in his mind a long time. "It's been almost two years since I've seen any boys or girls from Oidak. Aren't they going to come any more?"

Mr. Parker gave him a long look, then answered brusquely, "No, I guess not."

"Why?" Pablo asked, although Mr. Parker's attitude did not encourage questions.

"Maybe they don't want to learn the things we teach."

Strange answer, thought Pablo, but he waited silently.

"That's all, Pablo. If you change your mind in the next day or two, let me know." Pablo nodded and walked out onto the wide porch. He stood looking at the green trees, lawns, and flowers, and the water flowing on them.

o   o   o

Seven days later Pablo, with the rest of his class, marched across the wide green lawns to the auditorium of the main building for graduation exercises. The girls were wearing white dresses they had made. They had tied their hair with gay ribbons. The boys, in white shirts and dark trousers, were wearing ties for this great occasion. Everybody was a little excited and a little frightened.

The teachers had chosen Pablo to give the class speech. Just why, he could not figure out. He felt no brighter than most of the other students in the class. Maybe it was because he had never shirked his work, had tried to obey the rules, had learned to speak good English, and could memorize well.

Pablo found himself seated on the stage of the auditorium with thirteen other graduating boys and girls from the tenth grade. Out of all those who had come and gone in those five years, these were all who were left to graduate. They looked down upon rows of younger students, seated according to class groupings by school staff members, who now manned the ends of rows to insure order.

In rows further back sat a few townspeople, invited by staff members to the exercises.

For a while there was only a buzz of whispering voices, with occasional stifled laughter and coughs. Then Mr. Parker walked through the auditorium and up the steps to the center of the stage and stood waiting for silence. He gave a signal. Everyone stood up. The school band loudly struck up "America the Beautiful." Everyone tried to sing in tune with it, but Pablo could hardly hear his own voice in the din. Then everyone sat down.

As Pablo sat waiting for his cue he went over in his mind just what he was supposed to say. He remembered how frightened he had been on his first day at school—a lot more frightened than he was now. He grinned an inward grin.

Daring thoughts flashed through his head. Could he put aside the speech he had learned and say things he really thought? Why not? This was his graduation. He would not say: "Tonight I will tell you how much this school has meant to me." He would say: "Here we are no longer free to roam our hills and desert. Here we mustn't touch the flowers and plants; they are not ours. Here boys and girls must never speak their own loved languages. Here we must listen to white American teachers speak with loud scratchy voices. Here we learn to use expensive machines we do not have at home. Here we learn how to live as white men— not to make better use of what we have on our reservations. Here precious water is wasted that could be used for crops."

Blanket Indian

Applause for the speech Mr. Parker had been making snapped his thoughts back to the present. He knew he could not carry out his deep desire. Five years of strict obedience to orders could not be scrapped so easily. When he heard his cue, he walked to the front of the class and started his speech.

He remembered exactly all the words that the white teachers had wanted him to say. He joined in the song and finally, when the name Pablo Red Deer was called in the handing-out of diplomas, he stood again and walked calmly forward to get his. Now he was not afraid to stand up when his name was called.

government property

The boarding school

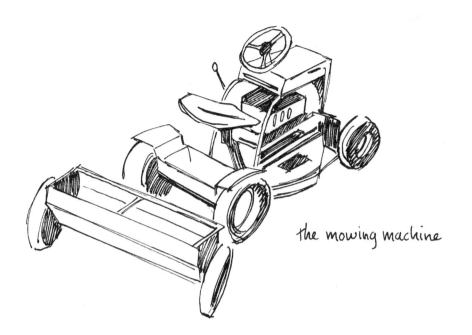

the mowing machine

the dances begin! (antelope clan)

Ralph's village

Hopi Kachina doll

the snake dance

Hopi people watch the dance
(holding their wigs on!)

a Navajo graduate back home.

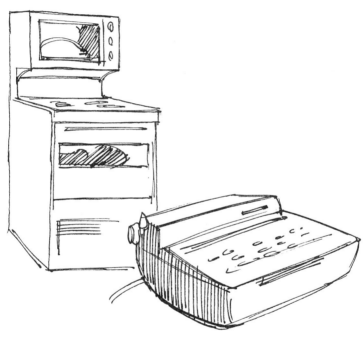

School skills !

White Man's World

1. "Indian" Jeweler

That night, after the graduation festivities, Pablo lay in his narrow bed listening to the breathing of sleeping companions. Tomorrow we'll all be leaving, he thought. What shall I do next?

He turned, deeply troubled. He was sure he had not learned in five years at the Big School the things his grandfather had expected him to learn in two. Why? He looked into himself for the reasons. I have tried to learn through books. I have worked with other boys on the grounds and gardens—under supervision. I have supervised younger boys on ground work and in the dormitory. Could I work with older Indian men? Here I have directed young boys. On the reservation, to be of any help, I must be able to lead and direct men.

His next thoughts overwhelmed him. Here I

have learned from Mr. Tanner how to tell when
the plants need water; how to turn water from one
irrigating ditch to another; but I have not learned
the things our people need most—how to develop
water and bring it to where it is needed. That's the
really important thing. How do white men do this?

The more he thought about what he had learned
at school the more he realized he still lacked experience in the white man's world. What I really need
to learn the ways of the white men is to work with
them on a job.

A job, that's it. But what kind of a job could I
get? Gardener? Worker in the fields? I don't know
what else I could do. I don't even know I could get
any job at all in the world of the white man. Why
did Great Spirit make people of different colors
and races? Didn't he know this would cause grief?

Pablo tossed, trying to find answers to his questions.

Finally he decided on immediate action. He
must find a job of some kind—any kind.

He left his bed and dressed silently. There were
a few possessions of his own in his locker. These
he made into a bundle, and with this under his arm
he quietly left the dormitory. He walked swiftly
across the lawn to the street, and headed away

from the school. In the gray light of early dawn the city seemed quiet and peaceful.

Gradually, as he walked, the houses and yards gave way to stores—small stores at first, then larger buildings. Now he moved slowly along the streets, looking curiously at displays in windows. One tall plate-glass window gave him a mirror-like view of himself.

It showed him a youth, tall, wide-shouldered, narrow hips, no extra flesh on his long bones. Heavy black hair. Wide-set dark eyes, eager and intent under black brows. How different he was from the thin, frightened lad who had come to the Big School five years ago!

He kept walking. Near noon, he realized he was hungry, but had no money to buy food. In a park he found a drinking fountain. The clear cool water tasted fine. He sat down on a shady bench to rest, and must have slept, because when he awakened the sun was low in the sky.

He had wasted a day and did not have a job. He walked along the street toward the setting sun. Maybe this way was a store or some place he could ask about a job.

Luck was with him. He saw an Indian boy, a Navajo, he had known in school a year or so before. What's his name?—Joe Bow. That's it. He called, "Hi, Joe!" The boy turned and, recognizing him, grinned.

"What you doin' here? Thought by this time you'd be a big track runner. Your leg still stiff?"

Pablo smiled. "Naw, thought I'd get a job for a while. You know of any jobs?"

Joe did not answer directly, but asked, "Where do you live—out this way?"

Pablo tried a lighthearted answer. "I don't have a place yet. I just left school this morning to hunt a job. I'll have to find a place when I get a job."

Joe looked at Pablo steadily. "Where'd you eat today?"

Pablo laughed. "I didn't." Both boys chuckled.

Then Joe said, "I live with my sister and her family not far from here. Come eat with us." When Pablo hesitated Joe said, "Plenty of food, not fancy, but plenty of it."

"I'd like to go," Pablo answered. He was hungry. Besides, he knew that Joe would be hurt if he refused the invitation.

When they reached his sister's small house at the edge of the city, Joe told the family, "This is Pablo. I knew him at school. He gave me some good tips on how to breathe and run so I won some races. He comes from the Papago reservation. He has no home here. No food today—no place to sleep tonight." Joe's sister and her children smiled at Pablo and moved over to make room for him at the table. As simply as that he became a member of this Navajo family.

After supper Joe said to Pablo, "You ever made any jewelry—silver rings and things like that?"

"No. My people make baskets, but not jewelry."

That didn't stop Joe. "Man I work for wants another Indian boy—maybe he'd take you. Could you learn to make jewelry?"

Pablo said quietly, "I could learn."

The next morning he went with Joe Bow to a shop in the city where Indian jewelry was sold. In a back room of the shop a number of people were working fast on various machines. Pablo was surprised to see that he and Joe were the only Indians. The white man listened to Joe, looked at Pablo and nodded. "Come with me." Pablo followed him to a bench. "You'll work here."

Pablo soon learned to cut small rectangles from a sheet of silver. These he passed to Joe Bow, who heated them glowing red, then hammered them into concave ovals ready for a white man, named Hank, to add an Indian design and finish them with a sheen. These were conchas for belts and for moccasin fastenings.

At the end of the week, the white boss handed each worker an envelope.

"Our pay," said Joe. "Open yours."

In the envelope Pablo found a bill and some silver change—the week's wages. He looked at Joe, grinned, put the bill in his pocket and walked gaily jingling the change in his hand. This was the first wage he had ever earned on a job away from school. With this, he knew he could buy things.

That night after supper, while he and Joe sat in the yard, Pablo asked a question that had been gnawing at him all week. "If this is not really Indian-made jewelry, why does this white man who owns the shop want any Indians at all working there?"

Joe laughed with a twisted mouth. "To help him sell more jewelry so he can make more money. When tourists ask if this is real handmade Indian jewelry, he likes to bring us in from the back room. No one ever gets into the workroom to see how the stuff is really made. After a while he may move you and me into the front of the shop where we will work a few hours each day so tourists can see us."

Pablo thought of the things he had watched being made on the machines—rings, necklaces, belts, pins. "Can't the people who buy these things see it is not the fine handwork of the Indians? The silver is thin—the turquoise is a light greenish-blue instead of the deep blue of the robin's egg."

"Looks all right to most white Americans; the designs are Indian. 'Factory-mass-produced imitations' is what the boss has to call it when he sells it in big lots to other stores or shops."

Pablo frowned. "I think it's wrong to cheapen real Indian-made silver things by selling these imitations to white Americans who don't know the difference. Can't the Indians who make good silver things do something about this trick?"

Joe sat silent a long time; then he said: "The white boss thinks it's a joke to outwit other white Americans." Then he added in a serious voice, "I have heard that some place Indians who make silver jewelry put a little sign on each piece to show it is Indian-made."

"Why don't you find that place to work? Look, Joe, while we have been talking here, you have drawn a design—a good design—with a stick in the dirt. You could make new designs for real Indian jewelry. We are helping this white man to be dishonest. Is this the way white men treat each other? It's no good."

Joe looked away but did not answer. Then he looked defiantly back at Pablo. "I work here because it is a job—because I have a purpose. I make good money. I am saving it to buy sheep when I get back to the reservation. There I'll get me a wife, build a house, have some kids. What more do I want? Nothing." He stood up, stretched, and yawned. Thought Pablo: He has a plan. I do not. I should not talk to him this way.

Joe stood a moment, then said, "We'd better get some sleep. Work tomorrow."

"I like to sleep out-of-doors. Been five years since I slept outside. O.K. if I sleep out here tonight?" Pablo asked.

Joe grinned. "Sure. See you in the morning." He went indoors.

But in the morning Pablo was not there. Before daylight he had put some money in a can, placed this on the doorstep, and noiselessly left.

2. Enemies of Coyote

Soon Pablo's legs and mind were stepping along the highway heading north. He had left no message, but hoped Joe would understand why he could not stay on working at something he thought was shoddy and wrong. He could see Joe's reason for staying. But having a family and enough sheep to make them a living—that was not what he, Pablo, wanted.

When he mastered more of the white man's way of doing things he would go home too, to follow in the footsteps of his grandfather. He would discard some old ways and teach the people new ways he had learned. But cheating others with cheap imitations wasn't what he wanted to bring home to his people, so staying here was a waste of precious time.

"Hey! look where you're going!" a man's voice boomed near him.

Pablo jumped back and looked around. A white man was standing by a pickup truck at the gate of an enclosure marked "XWL Construction Company." Out of the gate had just rolled a huge machine.

Pablo grinned at the man who had shouted to him. "Guess I was lost in my thoughts."

The man looked closely at this dark-skinned boy. "Where are you going?"

Pablo hesitated—"I'm hunting a job."

"Where'd you come from?"

Pablo ignored this direct question. "I just finished school. Like to get a summer job some place."

The man smiled. "You speak good English for a Mexican boy. Must have been going to school in the States." Pablo obligingly nodded.

"Want a job as flagman for the summer? We're short a man."

"What would I be doing?" Pablo asked.

"You'd be at one end of this construction job to keep cars from coming through until the road is clear of our construction machines and men. Someone signals you when to let the cars come and when to stop them. There has to be a man at each end; we've got only one man signed on now. You get your meals, a tent to sleep in, and four dollars a day—Sundays off."

Pablo turned the idea over as the man talked. He certainly would need to get food and a place to stay. Maybe this would be a good deal.

"I'll take it." Pablo answered. "How do I get there?"

"Get in the truck. You can ride with me. Name is Bill Jackson. What's yours?"

"Pablo."

"Have to have a last name for the payroll—Gonzales? Martinez? Hernandez? I'll bet yours is one of those."

Pablo Red Deer smiled. "The first one you said will do."

Bill laughed. "Knew I'd hit it. You Mexicans are all called Gonzales, Martinez or Hernandez."

They drove fast until they caught up with a caravan of cars and highway equipment, then poked along behind it until, in the late afternoon, they passed a canyon and reached a place where a permanent camp was set up. Bill Jackson introduced Pablo to several of the men as "This is our new flagman, Pablo Gonzales."

One of the men showed Pablo a tent where he

would sleep with a few others. As the men got settled, Pablo listened and watched.

The next morning someone gave him an orange-colored jacket, a white helmet, and a red flag, and stationed him a short distance from where a big bulldozer was starting to work. "Be sure to keep cars back until we signal you to let them come through."

Pablo nodded. Left to himself, he looked down at his orange jacket. "Now I have power," he thought, with a thin smile of self-derision.

At the end of the day he asked one of the men, "How long will we be working here?"

"Until we finish this section of the road up to the Utah line."

"Utah"—Pablo was puzzled. "Is this Utah?" he asked.

The man started to laugh. Then noting the demand in Pablo's black eyes, he answered seriously, "No, we are in northern Arizona, not far from the Utah-Nevada line."

o   o   o

After supper that night some of the men gathered around the campfire smoking and talking.

Pablo, sitting a little apart, suddenly heard the word "coyote." He moved closer, not wishing to miss anything they were saying.

"There are coyotes around here all right," one man said. "Last time we were here I heard them almost every night. We didn't have any traps though."

"Bill brought traps this time," a second man said.

Pablo thought—Bill? Could this be Bill Jackson, the man he had ridden with? Would Bill trap a coyote and make it suffer?

"Don't really need traps," a third man said. "We can shoot them."

"Better to trap them and knock them in the head to kill them," said the first man. "Bullet holes hurt the sale of the hides."

"Can you sell hides without ears? We can get two-fifty bounty for each pair of ears."

"Oh, sure. If someone wants ears on the hide, a good taxidermist 'll make 'em out of little pieces of hide and fur. How many traps did you bring, Bill?"

"Couple a' dozen. They're all in a gunnysack in the pickup. Better wait to set them until the moon comes up so we can see, but you fellows be sure to fasten them tight to a little tree or something or the coyote will thrash around and get the trap loose, then there goes your trap and your coyote."

"Can gnaw off the foot that gets caught too, I've heard," one of the men said.

"Yeh, but at least you don't lose your trap."

A great resolve was forming in Pablo's mind. He must find those traps and he must destroy them before these men could set them. The pickup truck stood in the shadow of one of the big bulldozers. He got up casually and walked toward it, but when he was about to climb into the back, someone called, "Hey, kid, where you going?" Pablo jumped and mumbled something about getting his jacket. Then he turned and walked to the tent where he was supposed to sleep.

After he had waited a while he tried again. Maybe the way would be clear now. The men were still laughing and talking around the fire, but the moon would soon be up.

He crept out of the tent making no sound. Twenty feet to the truck, and anyone looking could see. Pablo had to take that chance. Seven silent steps. He made it. Now he was pulling himself into the pickup. The gunnysack was there. He grasped the sack and moved it a little. It was very heavy. It was the traps all right. He knew he could

carry them if he could get the sack out where he
could lift it on his back. He took off his jacket and
arranged it over the pickup's tailgate to deaden any
noise.

Just then one of the men came stumbling up the
path. He went right past the tailgate of the truck.
Pablo curled up like another gunnysack. The man
went by without noticing—but would he on the
way back? The wait seemed endless. Then Pablo
heard him coming again. An empty bottle clattered
on the floor of the truck beside Pablo and a hand
grasped the tailgate padded by Pablo's jacket. For
a minute the man teetered, then steadying himself,
he staggered back to the fire.

Pablo got to work again. He got the sack onto
the jacket, slipped past it onto the ground, and
carefully listened. So far all seemed safe. He
stooped and managed to get the sack on his back
and ease himself up. Slowly he edged to a cluster
of low trees on the far side of the camp, where he
paused to adjust the weight of the sack on his back.
Then he started at a swift trot toward the edge of
a canyon he had seen as they rode into camp.

He had to destroy these traps, but how? Break-
ing them with rocks would make too much noise.
Then how else? As he crept to where he could

look over a ledge he got his answer. First he heard a faint swirling, gurgling sound; then far below he made out a rushing of water over steep rocks. If he could get the traps down into this waterfall they might never be found, or if they were found they would be too rusty to use.

He lugged the sack to a high place almost directly over the falls, and a mighty push sent it out into clear space and crashing and splashing into the falls below.

He crawled back over the ledge to the flat land above. The pale moon was beginning to show. Soon the men will be hunting for their traps. He thought, "I'd better circle back, get into bed, and pretend to be asleep when they start looking for the traps."

At a clump of cedars he stopped. There was a murmur of men's voices. He ran to the nearest tree, grabbed a lower branch and pulled himself up among the thick, low-hanging limbs. The voices were angry. "He's hiding somewhere with those traps."

"Hey! I've some hound dogs back home. They'd take one whiff of this jacket he left and track him to the Mexican border even."

A second voice answered, "He couldn't go far.

Those traps are too heavy. It'll take him hours to lug them into town to sell or trade. Might as well wait until daylight."

"Bill shouldn't have picked up the little tramp. You can never trust foreigners."

Foreigner?—me? Pablo thought. Then he chuckled. My people were here before his.

Pablo waited until he could no longer hear the sounds of feet, then he climbed slowly down and sat crouched on the ground at the foot of the tree. Where should he go? Not back to camp, that was for sure.

He rubbed his hands together. The late spring nights in this northern country were cold, and he missed his jacket. He knew he must get going, but where? Maybe Mr. Jackson will send the white police after me to get the traps. But they won't catch me if I stay away from the highway and stick close to the foothills, unless that man sends home for his dogs.

The ground was now flooded with moonlight.

To go away from where the construction camp was located, he must head west. He looked up at the stars to get his directions.

He was sure he could find water in the hills. Food? There must be some kind of berries or something he could eat. One thing he knew: Indians were smarter than white men about ways to live in desolate rough country.

Other thoughts came as he fell into a rhythmic lope. Maybe I should have tried to talk to Mr. Jackson and persuade him not to trap coyotes. But even if I had, he could not have convinced the men. They all wanted to kill coyotes—all of them. Was Black Fox right? Are the ways of white men bad? He wouldn't want to take the ways of these white men back to his people.

"He-Who-Runs-Far?" he thought. "Here he is running like a hunted coyote from the white men he is supposed to learn from."

3. Moving Man

ooooooooooooooooooooooooooooooooooooooooooooooooooooooooooooooooooooooooooooooooooooooooooo

All night Pablo went west, half walking, half running, guided by the stars. He felt safe—must be twenty miles between him and the camp now. When the sun rose he stopped for a while to rest by a small, rippling creek. He found a clump of heavy brush, crawled in and slept. When he awakened, the heat of the day had passed. Night was coming on. He bathed his face and hands, drank deeply of water, and started on. Now he traveled away from the foothills toward the valley. He walked fast in the twilight, thinking about food. This was piñon country: berries later in the summer; piñon nuts in the fall. Just the wrong time of year to find much to eat. But maybe some of these streams had trout.

He was walking along in the gathering darkness,

thinking how he might catch a fish, when he stopped suddenly. Did he smell coffee on the faint little breeze that was blowing? No, of course not. Thinking about food was making him imagine things. Then he was hit by a fear that somehow he had walked in a circle back toward the construction camp. His sense of direction assured him this was not so, and the stars confirmed that feeling. Yet, he was now really sure he smelled coffee. His first impulse was to turn back into the hills, but hunger and curiosity urged him on. He came to a clearing, and there a man was squatting over a small fire, stirring something in a pan. On the coals a coffeepot bubbled. Pablo, seeing the man rise to his feet, drew back hurriedly. The man's hand flew to a gun holster on his hip.

"Who's there?" His voice was level and without panic.

Pablo hesitated, then stepped forward into the firelight.

"You alone?" the man asked, eyes steady, his hand still on the gun.

"Yes, sir." Pablo suddenly was not afraid. This man would only hurt another if he must protect himself.

"What are you doing way out here on foot?"

The man peered at him more closely. "No gun. You're not hunting."

"Got lost," Pablo said briefly. The man looked at him with a skeptical smile. "Hungry?" he asked crisply, noticing that Pablo had not been able to keep his eyes away from the cooking-pan over the fire.

"Yes, sir. Very hungry."

The man laughed and walked to the fire. "Plenty of stew here, such as it is." He filled a tin plate and handed it to Pablo. "Help yourself to coffee." He indicated a tin cup nearby. They ate silently. The man asked no questions. When they finished, they sat watching the dying fire.

The man sighed and stood up. "Now maybe you can help me." He led the way up a bank to a gravel road. There a large moving van was pulled off to the side with a flat tire on the front wheel. "No one has come along this road since I got here a little after noon, until you dropped from the sky." He grinned, and Pablo answered with a quick smile. "Usually have a second man along, but we're short of help and I can't do these things as easily as I used to." Pablo had noticed the man's right hand had only the index finger and thumb. Even with the two of them the job wasn't easy.

"There, we got it. Now I'll get on the road and try to make up some time." He looked at Pablo speculatively. "I'm going east as far as Chicago. Can I give you a lift?"

Pablo thought quickly. He couldn't risk traveling back along the road past the construction camp he had just fled. "Which road are you taking?" he asked.

"Due north from here to Salt Lake City, then east by way of Cheyenne and Omaha." Pablo figured this way would be a little west of the construction camp, but he wasn't sure. "Yes, I'd like a ride," he answered.

The man held out his hand. "My name's Walker," he said. "Bob Walker." Pablo shook hands lightly.

"I am Pablo." Then he added softly, "Red Deer."

For a while they joggled along the gravel road. On the highway they got rolling. Bob made some attempts at conversation, outroaring the truck. Pablo answered politely, but as briefly as he could.

"You don't talk much, do you?"

Pablo grinned, gave the man a fleeting look— "My grandfather says people who talk too much tell lies."

176

The man laughed. "Your grandfather was probably right. You're an Indian boy?"

"Yes. Papago." Pablo waited for the vague look people usually gave when he said Papago.

"Arizona, close to Tucson. Big reservation. Biggest in the U.S., isn't it?"

Pablo wondered how this man knew as much as he did about his homeland. "Second largest," he answered.

"How large is it in acres?"

"Well, it is 2,855,923 acres in all," Pablo answered.

"Whee! I knew it was big—I used to drive a van from San Diego to Phoenix. I went through a lot of Papago country."

After a time the man asked, "You headed to school some place?"

"No." Pablo waited a few minutes. "I am going to get a job."

"Want to tell me where?"

"I don't know. Any place."

"Can you drive a car?"

"Not much. A tractor—a little."

"Say, could you unload and load heavy furniture?"

"Yes. I'm strong. I can do heavy work."

177

"Tell you what—when we get to Salt Lake City I'll ask our warehouse man if he can use you to help the drivers unload and load our vans. Pay is pretty good, and the last time I was there they were looking for good workers."

"I'd like that job," Pablo said.

So when they got to Salt Lake City, Mr. Walker went in to talk with the warehouse supervisor. He was gone a long time and came out grim-faced. Even before he spoke, Pablo felt sure there was no job here.

"Don't need anyone here, Pablo. Have more men than they can use. Want to ride on with me as far as Cheyenne, and see whether there is a job there?"

Pablo hesitated, looked around at the tall buildings on every side, felt nervous because of the strangeness of the big city, and said quickly, "I'd like to go on with you if it's all right—I must get a job."

"Fine, you can help me if we have any trouble with the van; you're a good man to have along. Now, we'll go get a good meal before we start on. Tonight we'll sleep along the road at a truck stop I know."

Pablo hesitated. He was very hungry, but he

178

knew eating in a restaurant cost money. He didn't have any. "Guess I'll just wait for you here in the truck," he said.

Mr. Walker smiled. "I figure I owe you something for helping me with the truck. The meals on this trip are on me."

With an answering smile, Pablo followed Mr. Walker into the restaurant.

o   o   o

From Salt Lake City the big van rolled smoothly along canyon roads and over steep mountain highways through rugged and beautiful mountain ranges. It was the season when high-level snow was melting, and small creeks gurgled and danced below the side of the highway. Here and there a few spring flowers were showing.

Pablo talked even less than usual—his eyes and mind trying to see and hold the majesty of these great mountains, many still topped with snow. As they rounded a curve, new mountain heights came into view and he drew a quick sharp breath.

"Not frightened, are you?"

"No." Pablo smiled, then said quietly, "I have never been in snowy mountains like this."

"We'll make it all right. This old van has lots of power."

Pablo only nodded, but his mind picked up the word "power." Power, he thought, something inside that makes it possible to accomplish a thing; makes it possible for this rig to get where it's headed for. Maybe that is what our older people got from something. Then his eyes caught a clump of blossoming trees. "What kind of trees are those growing near the creek—those trees with red blossoms?" he asked.

"Those are balsam poplars; about the first trees here to blossom in the spring."

"When those blossoms wither are there fruits on those trees?" Pablo asked.

"No, after the blossoms fall, shiny, yellow-green, sweet-smelling leaves come. No use that I know of—but pretty to look at." Mr. Walker looked at Pablo from the corner of his eye and Pablo smiled—glad to know that this white man liked the things of nature. After that, Pablo became absorbed in new and strange things along the roadside, and Mr. Walker did not try to interrupt his thoughts.

Before noon the contour of the land changed. Pablo saw an oil derrick and asked, "What is that?"

"Oil derrick for pumping oil up out of the earth. We are in Wyoming now. Lots of oil here, and iron ore. Coal mining too in this part of the state. Seems to me when the Indians owned this land here, they used to trade crude oil to the emigrants going west to grease the axles of their wagons."

Pablo turned to face Mr. Walker. "Indians own this land? What tribe?"

"Guess the government owns most of the part that used to belong to the Indians. They say the Crow Indians were here more than a hundred years ago. Used to grow corn, beans, and pumpkins along the Powder River. Later other tribes came— Arapaho, Sioux, Cheyenne, Shoshone, and some more. Seems to me this country used to be hunting grounds for about twelve tribes."

"Are any of these Indians still here? Do they still raise corn and beans?"

"There's a reservation in this state called Wind River. Think only Arapahos and Shoshones live there. Guess some Indians have small farms in different places in the state." Mr. Walker was quiet a few minutes, then continued. "You know, Pablo, this land we're going through now used to be called part of the Great American Desert, and people thought you couldn't raise anything here. But now they grow lots of things: alfalfa, wheat, corn, potatoes, barley, apples, and some of the finest sugar beets grown anywhere in the United States."

"Must have lots of water," Pablo said quickly.

"Well, they have two kinds of farming: one is farming by irrigation and the other is dry farming. Some parts of the state get irrigation water from rivers fed by melting snow in the mountains; but other parts of the state are very dry and the people have had to learn to raise crops with very little water—just what they get from rainfalls. That's what they call dry farming."

"How did they learn?"

"I don't really know—built some kind of ponds to store rain water, I think."

By late afternoon the van was passing through a countryside that had no oil derricks or signs of mining. Instead, on both sides of the highway, there were freshly plowed fields. Pablo sniffed the pungent fragrance and felt good. It reminded him of Pagago fields after a rain.

"What will they plant in all these fields?" he asked.

"Sugar beets." Mr. Walker paused.

"When do they plant them?"

At this show of interest Mr. Walker gave some

details. "The weather is good now, so the ranchers will get them in right away. I've noticed a few cars already coming in bringing people to work in the fields. Each year people come here from other places to plant, thin, irrigate, and harvest beets. Lots of hand labor required, so some bring their whole families. Children, parents, and grand-parents sometimes work together. Each family tends about ten acres, I think. Mostly Spanish-Americans and Mexicans come; stay for the season, then move on. Call themselves migratory workers, but people around here mostly call them 'sugar tramps.'"

Pablo asked, "Where do these whole families live when they come—do they build houses, or are there houses from last year?"

"Most of the companies who own this land have sort of camps of little houses for their workers—just kind of shacks, I guess. I don't know much about it."

Pablo asked next, "How do these people, these 'sugar tramps,' learn this work?"

"Oh, I guess the ones who have been here before show the newcomers. Then there's a supervisor living on the ranch, who knows all about raising and harvesting beets."

"Does the supervisor know about what you call 'dry farming'?"

"Well I think most of the supervisors from these big places have studied at college and learned how to grow sugar beets and other things, by dry farming as well as by the irrigation they have here."

This set Pablo to thinking. If he could just work in a place where he could see such people he might learn something of the white man's magic. He would like to try.

In early dusk Pablo saw the tops of tall buildings looming ahead. "What town is that?" he asked.

"Laramie," said Mr. Walker. "The highway doesn't go through the town, just the edge of it. We'll stop at a place a little way the other side of Laramie, get supper and a place to sleep. Getting hungry?"

Pablo did not answer immediately. Finally he said slowly, "Would it be all right if I didn't go on to Chicago with you? I've worked in fields and— I think I'd like to work here." He grinned. "Maybe I could be one of those 'sugar tramps.'"

Mr. Walker, after Pablo's eager questioning, showed no surprise at this request. "Sure, if you think you'd like to work here, I'll let you off about a mile down the road where the main road into

Laramie crosses this highway. You'll probably be able to get a ride into town from there; only about a mile to the outskirts."

Pablo smiled at him, then said, feeling a little bashful, "I am glad I know you. You have been my good friend. I wish I could see you again some-time."

"Pablo, I hope you will find a good job—it's been nice having you along, and I am glad to be your friend."

Mr. Walker pulled up at the crossroads, and Pablo started to scramble down from the van. "Wait a minute," Mr. Walker said, "I still owe you some money for helping me." His hand held out a ten-dollar bill.

Pablo hesitated, then said, "My meals wouldn't have cost that much between here and Chicago." They both laughed.

"Go ahead—take it. You'll need it to get started here." So without arguing, Pablo put the ten-dollar bill in his pocket.

There was something else he wanted to say. "I know there wasn't a job in that warehouse in Salt Lake City because I am an Indian," he told Mr. Walker, "but here I think it will be different."

Mr. Walker leaned down and took Pablo's hand

in a firm grasp. "I'm sure you'll get a job here. Now I better be moving along. Lots of miles between here and Chicago. Good luck to you, Pablo Red Deer."

The brakes released, the engine turned over, and the van was on its way. Mr. Walker cheerily waved to him, and Pablo found himself waving back. He was glad he had told Mr. Walker his real name. He watched the van fade out of sight, then he turned and set out along the road at a fast swinging walk that soon brought him to some small buildings in the outskirts of Laramie.

4. Indian Work

oooooooooooooooooooooooooooooooooooooooooooooooooooooooooooooooooooooooooooooooooooooooooooo

His hand closed over the ten-dollar bill in his pocket, Pablo passed several small eating places, hesitated and moved on. He came to one where no customers were eating. A plump middle-aged woman was cleaning the counter there. He started to go in, but stopped as his eyes caught sight of a window two doors away. "Unusual Indian Work" said a hand-printed sign.

"Indian work," Pablo snorted, "made by white men in a back room?" He walked over to the shop and pressed his face against the window to get a close look.

"Hayia!" the word burst forth as he saw a small basket near the back of the window—a basket that looked like a rabbit. There wasn't any doubt it was a Papago basket, though this shop was so far from

87

Arizona. Could it even be one his mother had made? He tried to enter the shop. The door was locked. Maybe the lady in the diner could tell him when the shop would be open.

He entered the restaurant. The woman stopped her work at the counter, looked keenly at him and spoke to him in Spanish.

"Can I eat here?" He answered in English.

She laughed and said in English, "If you have the money to pay, yes. At first I thought you were Mexican; that is why I spoke to you in Spanish."

Pablo ordered a sandwich and coffee. When she brought it she said, "You look like a Mexican boy, even though you don't speak Spanish."

"I am a Papago," Pablo said.

The woman looked puzzled. "You have folks here in Laramie?"

He said, "No, no folks here."

"Coming here to work in the fields then?"

"Yes," Pablo answered, "to work in the fields." He now asked, "The shop with the Indian things —when will the man be there?"

"José's," she said. "He lives in the back, but he's gone into town tonight. He'll be there in the morning." Pablo nodded.

He ate slowly. This was a warm, friendly place.

He did not know where he would spend the night. The woman seemed almost to read his thoughts.

"Three houses down is where some of the men like you without families stay. I guess you will be going to the fields with them on the truck. They eat here about five in the morning."

Paying for the meal, he asked, "Will José have that shop open that early?"

The woman laughed. "If you want to buy something, he'll open up before daylight. Just knock."

"I'll see you in the morning," Pablo said as he picked up his change.

"Not me. I work late. Another woman comes in early and cooks, and a girl called Rosie will be waiting on you fellows." Looking closely at Pablo she added, "Say, you know you are a little like Rosie—don't talk much, don't laugh a lot. She's a Navajo Indian."

Pablo repeated, "I am a Papago." The woman shook her head, obviously not sure of what she was hearing, then walked with him to the door to point out the right house. It looked deserted, but as he walked up its steps a tall white man sitting in the shadows stood up.

"I've come to work in the fields," Pablo said. "The lady where I ate sent me here to sleep."

"O.K. You'll have to share a room with three others. Where you from? New Mexico?"

"Down that way," Pablo agreed. What difference would it make to this man?

"Late getting in."

"Yes," agreed Pablo.

The next morning when Pablo headed in with the others to breakfast, he hurried ahead to pound on the door of the shop next to the café. When sleepy-eyed José opened the door, Pablo spoke quickly. "I want to see the basket in the window— the one that looks like a rabbit."

José handed it to Pablo and he examined it carefully: then excitedly Pablo asked, "How much?"

José had been carefully appraising Pablo. "Nice?" he beamed. "Cute little basket."

"Yes. How much? I have to get back to eat breakfast."

José hesitated. Pablo shifted impatiently. "Ten dollars." José watched Pablo's reaction.

Pablo was silent. He didn't have that much. He had paid for supper and bed out of the money Mr. Walker had given him, and knew he had to pay for breakfast. "Seven," he said. He thought, I'll bet my mother didn't get more than three or four dollars, maybe not that much.

"Eight," said José.

Without more talk Pablo hurriedly counted out almost all the money he had left and hurried to the restaurant.

A girl, younger than he had expected, set a place for him at the counter. She was a tall girl with high cheekbones, bronze skin, and slender hands. Pablo looked at the shining black hair held back from her forehead by a ribbon band as blue as the desert flax flowers. At the throat of her dress was a small silver pin with a true blue turquoise. This pin, a swift glance told him, was Indian made.

When Rosie brought his coffee, she glanced at him. Pablo felt something flash between them—a wordless interchange. She lowered her eyes and hurried to get food the men ordered.

After the meal, when the others started out, Pablo lingered. Unwrapping the rabbit basket he asked softly, "Would you keep this for me until I come back?"

Rosie was facing away, but turned. "Oh," she exclaimed. "You got that beautiful rabbit basket from José's shop." Her dark eyes were approving.

Pablo felt warm and gay. "It is a Papago basket. My mother in Arizona made it. I saw it last night in the window and thought maybe she'd made it.

This morning I found her special mark woven into the bottom. Don't know how it got way up here."

"José buys a lot of things from a trader. That is a beautiful basket; your mother is a good weaver. Yes, I'll keep it for you. It will be safe."

Pablo would have liked to talk longer, but the men were already getting into the truck.

As workers climbed aboard they gave their names to a check-off man holding a list. "Pablo Red Deer," Pablo said without hesitation, as he stepped up to get into the truck. The checker ran his finger down the list. "No such name here. Where'd they sign you on? Denver or Santa Fe?"

Pablo shrugged, muttered "Yes."

"O. K. Somebody slipped up, but we need every man we can get. Climb on."

°　　　°　　　°

Pablo looked around at his companions seated on the narrow board seats in the truck, men of different ages and races. He listened to what they said. Some had worked together on this place before and were glad to see each other. Some had families to support, a wife and children, parents, younger brothers and sisters. Others were without family ties. Men without families would live in a sort of dormitory. Well, Pablo knew about dormitories.

A man spoke to Pablo. "You new here?"

"Yes."

"You'll like working here. They treat you all right. There's enough good food. The supervisor is a good man."

Pablo smiled, nodded. He would behave the Papago way. Learn by watching, not by asking.

It was almost noon when the truck reached the dormitory. Each man went inside and selected a bed. Pablo was glad to get the one nearest the door. He liked to be able to turn onto one side in bed and not have to see some one else.

Near the dormitory was the combination cook-shack and dining room. As soon as the noon meal was finished, the men were called out to meet their field supervisor and get their work instructions.

This supervisor was a rangy man with no fat on him. A man not yet forty, Pablo guessed. He had red hair and wore a broad-brimmed straw hat pulled down low to shade his blue eyes. He spent a few minutes nodding to those he recognized from the year before, then turned to brief those who were new this season. His name, he said, was Jim Burnett. Then he got down to business.

Each family would have about ten acres to tend from planting time until fall harvesting. The single men had less—about six acres. In a short time he had assigned each man to a work area.

Earlier arrivals had already started planting. Pablo walked to where they were working and watched carefully. By the time the supervisor called his name to give him the seed he needed, he was sure he could do that job.

Pablo had not worked at stoop labor for a long time, and he had to get used to it. For several days he ached with every move he made. Pride kept him from complaining, and soon he was able to work long hours stooping as did the others. At night the tiredness of his body made sleep come quickly.

Through the summer they all worked from gray dawn to blue dusk. They worked in the hot sun and through flash summer rains. During the thinning they crawled down the long rows on hands and knees to pull out weak or unhealthy plants. Weeding too was done by crawling along the irrigated rows, carefully removing the weeds by hand to avoid lacerating the plant leaves.

At night the men fell into bed as soon as supper was over. In the morning they talked of the day's work ahead. In the fields they seldom spoke unless about the work. Pablo listened when he heard them talk, but seldom joined in. If others wondered about him they did not question. Here no one asked about the life of another.

Pablo worked steadily. He liked being entirely responsible for the plants in his particular plot—seeing that they grew strong and healthy. One hot day when the sweat was running down and stinging his eyes with its salt, he tore off the tail of his shirt and bound it around his head to catch the sweat and hold back his thick black hair.

Supervisor Burnett, coming by, grinned. "You look like one of those Hopi Indians from Arizona with that red band around your head." Pablo only smiled. "Your beets look good," the supervisor praised.

Pablo looked up. "Everything grows well when there is enough water."

"That's true. Good thing the government put in the big dam just above here. Canals bring it to where we can put it into ditches for these fields. Before we had this dam, growers used to hire a man to come and seed the clouds so we'd have enough water." He stood looking at Pablo. "Do you know about that?"

"No, I don't know." Pablo waited.

"Thought you Mexican boys might not. Well, it's too long a process to explain now." He turned to leave.

"I'd like to know." Pablo spoke earnestly. "I want to learn all I can about water."

The supervisor stopped, surprised. He peered into Pablo's serious black eyes. "Why?" he asked.

"I am an Indian. The land I come from is very dry. My people need water."

Mr. Burnett hunkered down on his heels, took off his big straw hat and wiped the sweat from his forehead. Pablo saw his shock of curly red hair was now darkened by sweat. His red hair makes his eyes seem more blue, Pablo thought, as the supervisor looked squarely at him.

"Where do you come from? Navajo country?" he asked.

"No. Papago. Southern Arizona. Desert country."

"What crops do you raise there?"

"Not much. Garden things—a little corn; lots of beans." Pablo's eyes twinkled. "Some call us the 'Bean People.'"

The supervisor laughed. "All your people as good workers as you?"

Indian Work

"Better." Pablo did not look up, but the supervisor saw a proud lift of his shoulders.

"Where do you get water for your gardens and crops?"

"Just rain. We depend on rain. Some years we don't get much. We never get enough water to grow crops like this. When it rains we try to catch and hold it in *charcos*—" He stopped. "Do you know about *charcos*?"

The supervisor answered frankly as Pablo had done a moment ago. "No, I don't know."

"Thought probably you white Americans wouldn't," Pablo replied. They both laughed.

"I have told you my name—Jim Burnett. What's yours?"

"Pablo." Then after a slight hesitation, "Pablo Red Deer."

The supervisor put out his hand. "Glad to know you, Pablo."

"Now Pablo, tell me about *charcos*."

Pablo grinned. "*Charcos* are holes dug in the ground to catch and hold rain when it comes, so the water will not all run off. Some years rain does not come at all; then our crops die and people suffer."

Mr. Burnett sat thinking a few minutes. "Seems

to me your people should learn some of the methods of dry farming that are proving successful."

"This dry farming is what I came here to find out about," Pablo answered. He shifted his position and continued gravely. "Mr. Burnett, my people have always believed the Great Spirit Eé toy will give us rain unless we offend him. Each summer the medicine men and other older men of the tribe sing sacred rain songs and send up prayers for rain after our people have purged themselves of evil thoughts to start a new year in peace and harmony."

Mr. Burnett began to speak, but checked himself to let Pablo continue.

Pablo said almost harshly, "Then sometimes rain comes quickly, almost a deluge. It may last three or four days. Or rain may not come at all." He looked away, then with some hesitation went on. "Now, I sometimes wonder whether the medicine men, who have studied weather conditions over many years, set a date for the rain ceremony when they know there will probably be rain. When rain does not come, I wonder if that's because they have made a mistake in their figuring."

Mr. Burnett nodded thoughtfully.

"Well," said Pablo, urgently, "now you see why

I need to know all I can learn about getting water on our land."

"Yes, I see." Mr. Burnett stood up. "Tell you what. Not far from here is an experimental farm. They are specializing in ways of dry farming and stock raising. They study soil erosion, crop rotation, even developing certain tools to use in dry farming. I'm going over there on Saturday. Would you like to go along? I'll be there all day. You can look around, and men there will be glad to answer all the questions you can ask."

"Yes," Pablo said eagerly, "I'd like to go."

"O. K. It's a long drive. Be at my house by six-thirty Saturday morning." As the supervisor turned to leave he grinned. "Think you can trust your plants alone all day?"

Pablo returned the grin. "Yes, sir. They have learned to behave."

"Saturday morning by six-thirty then. You know where my house is?"

"Yes, sir, I'll be there." Pablo squatted down to his work again. He found himself humming a chant—one of the religious chants his grandfather had taught him. He smiled.

Before six-thirty Saturday morning, Pablo, in freshly-washed work clothes, walked the mile from his dormitory to the supervisor's home, a long, low white farmhouse with sloping red roof, set amid green fields with a trickling creek of water behind it.

As he turned down the lane he saw Jim Burnett step out onto the wide porch.

"Had your breakfast?" the supervisor hailed, then quickly, "I'm sure you could have a cup of coffee with me before we start." He held the door open.

Inside, a tall dark-haired woman rose and came forward. "You are Pablo," she greeted him. "Jim told me you're going with him to see the experimental farm."

Before Pablo could answer, a small, brown-eyed boy came almost flying into the room to land in his father's outstretched arms. "This is Tim," Mr. Burnett said. "Tim, this is Pablo." Pablo reached out his hand doubtfully. Immediately the child put his small hand in Pablo's, reminding him warmly of Younger Brother. "Sit here," Tim directed.

Pablo looked questioningly at Mrs. Burnett. She nodded and said, "That's right. We told Tim you would sit there and have breakfast with us."

The breakfast was brief, the talk about the country and weather. Pablo thought, I'll bet they never before had an Indian eating with them. Probably wondered if I would know what a knife and fork were. Then he felt ashamed of these thoughts. Nothing in their words or manner had suggested he was other than one of them.

The day was one that Pablo would always remember. At the experimental farm he saw men trying new ways in preparing land, in planting and tending crops, in bringing water where it was needed. He learned that in Wyoming, when people had fields too small to raise certain crops successfully, they sometimes combined them with the fields of others to form pastures for cattle; they banded together into "cooperative grazing associations" to operate these pastures. Some of these groups had built stock dams to provide water for cattle. Pablo's thoughts flew to his reservation and to ways this might be used there.

On the ride back to the ranch, Pablo sat quiet, trying to organize in his mind the many things he had learned. How could they be made to work for his people on the reservation? This kind of achievement—this was indeed the magic of the white man. Here at last he had found it. Occasionally Jim Burnett glanced at Pablo's serious, thoughtful face, but he did not break the silence.

Finally Pablo did. "Mr. Burnett, could a person get a job there at that experimental farm?"

"The people there are all from our University, Pablo. They work under men who are experts in the various activities carried on. Some of the young men you saw will probably come back there to teach after they graduate from the University."

Pablo did not answer. After a few minutes Mr. Burnett said, "Pablo, would you like to go to the University and study agriculture?" Then as an afterthought, "You have finished high school?"

"No, only tenth grade in a government Indian school. Would the University take me?"

"You would have to finish high school first, but I think if you stayed on here and worked for the ranch while you were going to our local high school, you could probably be ready for the University after one school year and two summer terms. Then after a couple of years in the University, you could work summers on this experimental farm and complete your last two years of University work."

"How long would that take—altogether?"

"Five years, if all went well."

Pablo sat very still, turmoil growing in him. He wanted with all his being to do this thing—to learn

everything he could, so he could help the fields of
the reservation become like the fine fields here.
That would truly be using the white man's magic.

But five more years away from Oidak, from Pa
Vi? He already had gained some knowledge, and
his people needed it now. If he went back he would
tell Tall Bear of bringing water to crops—even to
homes for washing and bathing. He didn't know
how to do it yet but he did know it could be done,
even without the help of Eé toy.

He must not stay away now for the five years it
would take to learn. As soon as the sugar beets were
harvested he would go back.

He felt a surge of pleasure in trying to imagine
what would happen when he returned to his home
country.

Pablo became aware that the supervisor was
glancing at him from time to time. Maybe Mr.
Burnett could sense the struggle going on inside
him. Finally Pablo said: "I must go back to my
people. I would like to work here, go to high
school, then to your University. It would take too
long. My grandfather, whose place I will take, is
old. He needs me."

Mr. Burnett nodded. "In that case, I won't urge
you to stay. But if you should go back there, and

later decide you would like to go through the University here, don't let any lack of money keep you from doing this. I am sure we could get you a University scholarship when the time came. That, with money you could save from summer wages, would put you through."

Pablo thanked Mr. Burnett with his eyes. He said, "You have taught me much."

o o o

From now on Pablo worked with new energy. As his body and hands moved swiftly through the harvesting, his mind was planning what he would be able to do for the people when he got home. How happy his family would be! How much he could tell Younger Brother and Sister!

A mechanical harvester loosened the ground around the fine beets he had grown. Off came their green tops to go into silos to be used as food for stock. The gray-white beets went into trucks to the beet dump and from there by train to the sugar factory. I have helped grow food for people and for stock, thought Pablo proudly.

It had been a good season. The work was finished. The workers were all making plans for their next move. Some would go back to families waiting for them. Others would drift about until money was gone, then hunt work again. Those with families here were going immediately to other jobs.

When the workers were paid off and Pablo put his money in his pocket, he saw Mr. Burnett standing close to him.

"Good-bye, Pablo. You've done a fine job this summer. If you should ever want to come back to go to our high school and the University, remember I'll be glad to help you get started."

Pablo returned his firm handclasp and smiled. "I'll remember." He added with a grin, "When you come to our country, look me up. Oidak is small enough so you can stand anywhere in the village and call my name. I'll hear you."

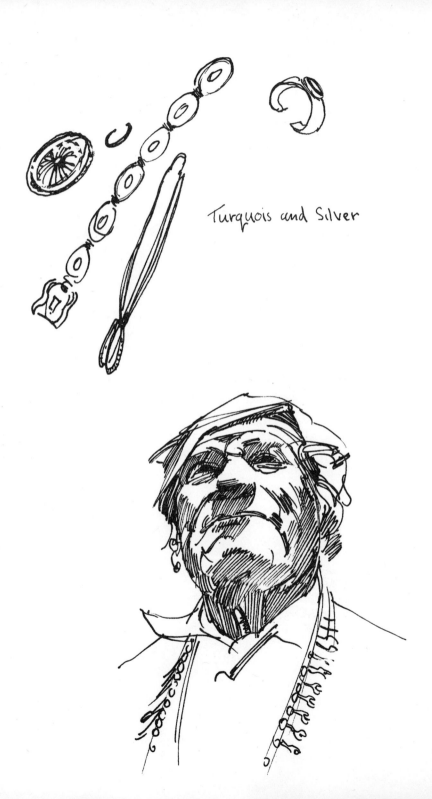

Turquois and Silver

White America

Genuine ?
Indian Jewelery

Trucking

a migrant field hand

Brahman stock used for crossbreeding to improve
cattle in arid regions.

white mans magic

Cactus wrens
on a cholla branch.

Sells had never looked so small

Coyote showed the way

Conflict of Worlds

1. Navajo Warning

When the bus reached Laramie, Pablo walked quickly to the cafe where Rosie worked. He was hurrying, he told himself, because he wanted to get his basket to take home with him.

Rosie's eyes welcomed him as he seated himself at the counter, and she hastened toward him. "You're back. I have kept the basket carefully. After work I will go home and get it for you."

Pablo smiled. "I want to take it back to my mother. I haven't seen her in six years. She'll be surprised to see that basket and know how it has traveled."

"You are going back to visit?" Rosie's eyes, under the straight, definite line of black eyebrows, narrowed.

"I am going back to stay. I want to give my

people the good things I have learned from the white man. I want to tell them how to get water on our land, to raise good crops to support our people, to grow better stock."

Rosie's smile faded. As he was speaking her eyes became black wells of disdain. "So you go to tell your people? Do you think they want to know what you go to tell them?"

Pablo sat very straight. "I go to take my grandfather's place. He is Governor and Keeper-of-the-Smoke in the village. He wants me to be a leader of our people. I—" Now Pablo cut himself short. Why had he spoken this way? Why had he bragged to this girl? He turned his eyes away, ashamed.

"If you will give me your order, please?" Rosie spoke calmly as though she had not heard his boasting.

But when he had finished eating and the restaurant was empty of others, she came to lean on the counter close to him. "Do you want to hear the story of a Navajo Indian girl—me?" she asked softly.

Pablo nodded. Rosie pushed his dishes aside and stood for a minute looking into space. Then she turned toward him. "When I was a very little girl

—four years old—so young that I don't remember much about being taken away from my family, I was sent with a bunch of other kids to an Indian boarding school. It was probably just like the one you attended—friends tell me all government schools are the same. Some kind of white officials took us. I remember being scared when they took us and for a long time afterward. I was put in a room with a Shoshone girl and a Choctaw girl. Of course we couldn't speak one another's language. Anyhow we all had to learn English."

Pablo nodded. "One way to make you learn English," he commented.

Rosie continued: "I learned to sleep in a regular bed, wear clothes like the white girls, read, write, figure. When I was ten or eleven, I learned to sew clothes on an electric sewing machine—"

Pablo interjected, "Make bread in an electric mixer, I'll bet."

Their laughter held a taste of bitterness. "Oh, yes! Wash clothes in an electric washer, iron with an electric iron. I can use all the gadgets of the white American. But by the time I had learned all this I had lost touch and forgotten the ways—even much of the language—of my family.

"At the end of my tenth year at school, the

woman vice-principal called me in and said I could
go home now and teach my people the ways of
the white man." Rosie's lips curled contemptu-
ously. "They never tried to teach us how to live
better as Indians on the reservation and be happy
there—just tried to make us over so we could live
like white people.

"My family could not read, so I wrote to the
trader asking him to let my father know I would
be home." Rosie drew a short breath. "When I got
off the bus a stranger was sitting on a burro waiting
for me. He said he was my father. This proved
true. He had a second burro—for me. No saddle,
of course. I straddled the burro. We were off. We
rode all day—sand, wind, heat. I couldn't understand half the things my father said during all those
hours. By the time we reached the hogan that was
home, my father was angry with me. I was dis-
gusted and homesick for the school.

"I didn't recognize my mother. When she told
me that I would start herding the sheep and goats
the next day, I didn't know what to say. But after
ten years in the world of the white man, I knew I
couldn't go back to herding sheep in bitter cold
or in burning hot sand storms, wade mud in pour-
ing rain to find a stray lamb, cook on a pile of

stones on the ground, sleep on a stack of dirty sheep skins. No water for washing clothes or bathing.

"Next morning I was long gone. I left the burro at the place where I caught a bus. I don't know if my father got her back.

"I got a job waiting table in a cafe in a California town. I wasn't fifteen yet. They didn't know or care about that. I was a good worker. Before long I got lonesome and wrote to the Shoshone girl I had roomed with at school. She wrote back telling me about this cafe. She thought I could make more money here. I've been working here a year now. I don't make more money, but I like the Mexican woman who owns this place. No yelling or scolding here. I have a nice room in the home of this Mexican woman. I get along all right, but sometimes I wonder whether I needed ten years of school to wait table."

Pablo didn't answer. Rosie's eyes had left his and she now stood looking far into the past. "Have you ever seen the Navajo children—just babies—herding sheep and goats, plodding along in the sand or straddling a skinny little burro?"

"No," said Pablo, "I don't know Navajo country—but Navajo friends at school told me about it. My home land is much the same—no water. Dry land. Sage and cactus. We depend on rains that do not come. Water is what we all need for our land."

Their eyes met. Rosie laughed a short mirthless laugh. "Yeh! Try and get it."

"There are ways—" Pablo leaned forward eager to explain. "I have finally learned ways of getting water and I will take this knowledge to my people."

"Try telling the old ones your ideas. Hear what they say to you." She spoke in a voice that matched the forthright look in her eyes. "You say you have been away more than five years. In all that time you have never seen them. Now it is too late. You have changed. You could not live in the old way now. You could not learn again to be a reservation Indian."

Pablo looked down. His lips tightened. He had learned to quiet such thoughts within himself. Why should he be disturbed by them again?

"I am going back to my people. I will follow in the paths of my ancestors. I will take my people the magic I was sent away to get. I will be a good Governor and Keeper-of-the-Smoke."

Small spots of color flamed on Rosie's cheeks. "I'll bet you still think power is a gift the gods hand out in a dream to someone who is worthy because he has run in the desert until he fainted. You haven't learned much in the five years you have been away. Can't you see that people, no matter what color or race, finally get what our people call power or magic because they believe in themselves, because they patiently work and study to keep a goal before them—a goal to reach?"

Pablo carefully counted out coins to pay for his meal. He tried to control his anger. But he ended by throwing the money on the counter and slamming out of the cafe.

"Your basket!" Rosie called after him, running to the door with it, but he had disappeared into the night.

2. He Speaks as a White Man

On the way from the cafe to the bus station, Pablo told himself: "I'll show her I can become a reservation Indian again. As soon as I take my grandfather's place as Governor and Keeper-of-the-Smoke, I will teach the people what I have learned. I will guide their talk and change their ideas about some of the superstitions they now have. They will accept the knowledge I bring from the white man's world. We will have water to use for our crops and in our homes; we will have better sanitation. I will find how to get it. And we will grow enough food every year."

On the southbound bus to his home country, he resolutely dreamed how all these things would come about. He no longer let himself have doubts about returning.

He Speaks as a White Man

At one bus stop he found a barber shop and had his black hair neatly trimmed.

Early on the third morning the bus dropped him off on the highway from where he could walk to Oidak. He had put on a blue shirt and gray slacks. He stepped briskly across the desert, his suitcase swinging at his side.

As he neared the village he saw a young man riding toward him on a burro—Ricardo Wells, the boy who had promised to tell Tall Bear that Pablo was staying longer. That was three years ago. Ricardo was bigger, heavier now.

"Hello," Pablo called.

Ricardo stopped. Across his lap was an old-fashioned handmade hoe. He carried a small package of lunch and a canteen of water.

"On your way to the gardens?" Pablo asked.

Ricardo looked with unfriendly eyes, but did not answer.

Pablo laughed. "Ricardo, don't you know me? I am Pablo Red Deer."

Ricardo spat into the sand. "Why did you come back? Get hungry in the white man's world?"

Pablo disregarded the sneer. "I came back because I have learned things that will help us to live better here."

Ricardo gave a vigorous kick to the burro's sides. "We do all right if we are left alone."

Pablo shook his head. Teaching new ways to his people might be hard if even the boys who had also been to the Big School were determined to follow old ways.

As he continued toward the village he felt a wind rising—stirring dust devils close by. He saw a youth about his age walking across the desert toward him. Pablo stopped. The boy looked at him closely, then said: "Say, you're Pablo Red Deer, aren't you? I went to the Big School one year when you were there. I was one of the last boys sent from this village. I am Miguel Benito."

Pablo put out his hand. Miguel touched it lightly, then asked doubtfully, "What are you doing here at Oidak?"

Pablo wondered why both boys had asked this question. This was where he had planned to return. This was the village of his grandfather, the Governor.

"I have come home."

He waited for some response. Miguel seemed to be struggling to say something. Finally he spoke earnestly. "Have you heard from your grandfather lately?"

"No! He is all right, isn't he? He is alive?" Pablo's voice tensed.

"Yes. He lives. But his life has changed since you left this village." Miguel turned hastily and walked away.

Pablo lowered his head against the wind and continued on his way.

o   o   o

When Pablo came in sight of his grandfather's home he paused to look at familiar things. A flood of memories washed over him. He saw the twisted old mesquite tree where he sat with his grandfather to learn so many of the old ways and beliefs, and where his mother, long before, had sat to weave baskets.

The door of the house swung open. Tall Bear stepped out.

"Grandfather," Pablo called happily. "I am back!"

Tall Bear looked around but gave no sign of recognition.

Pablo walked closer. He is old. He does not see well, Pablo thought. "It is Pablo—Don't you know me? I have returned." Maybe he does not hear well

227

now. Louder: "I have come back to Oidak. I have learned many things."

Tall Bear's frame was still straight and dignified. But though the morning sun shone full on the old man's wrinkled face, Pablo could see no smile.

The house door opened again. "Grandmother!" he called when he saw Shining Leaf standing in the doorway. She stepped inside again and closed the door.

Unbelieving, Pablo looked at his grandfather. Tall Bear was sizing him up carefully.

"You sent me to the Big School," Pablo said in careful English, "I have returned with knowledge I traveled far to get."

Tall Bear's eyes studied him. "Speak," he said finally, "speak in the tongue of your people."

Pablo looked at him in surprise. "You do not wish me to use English—the language you sent me to learn?"

"When you talk with Papago people, do them the courtesy of speaking their language—if you can still remember it."

So, in the Papago language, Pablo told Tall Bear his story—things he had done, things he had learned, lastly the many changes he thought could be made in the lives of the people.

He Speaks as a White Man

Tall Bear listened, his face impassive. He did not invite Pablo to sit. He too remained standing while Pablo poured out his long story. It was Pablo who finally suggested they sit together under the old mesquite. When his grandfather sat down he seemed to be acting against his will.

Meantime the village grapevine had been busy. Word had spread that Pablo, grandson of Tall Bear, was back at last. Old men gathered slowly to stand or squat within earshot near the mesquite tree openly listening while Pablo continued to give his report to Tall Bear.

As Pablo talked they looked at one another, stirred, shifted about and exchanged whispers and mutterings.

Bothered, Pablo paused at times to think how he could best go on with his story. In these pauses he could make out what the men were saying.

"The boy has not forgotten our language. But his voice is loud. His talk is fast like that of the white man. He does not know the ancient ones dug many miles of canals with sticks. He does not know that this offended Great Spirit so that all water disappeared." Pablo caught other murmurings. "We cannot herd Eé toy's raindrops into pipes to use as we wish." "This one speaks like a white man, he will cause our springs to go away." "Windmills take good water from under the land, and the land turns white." "If our young people keep to the old ways, Great Spirit will give us rain." "We will listen to the words of our medicine men, not to this one who has already offended Great Spirit."

In spite of these murmurings, Pablo kept on to the end of his story. When he had finished, the men moved quietly away, leaving him alone with his grandfather.

Tall Bear then spoke: "Before you left this village you were instructed in Papago traditions and sacred rites so you would not forsake the beliefs of our people. I said you should stay two years at the Big School to learn English and the magic of the white man. You stayed five years. You, who knew from my teachings that among Papagos no one tries to be better than his fellow men, stayed longer than any boy from Oidak ever stayed at the Big School. Then you left to work in the world of the white man.

"After two whole years at school, we expected you to bring back knowledge helpful to this village. You only sent word you were staying on. You did not ask me. You did not get permission of our council. Yours was the behavior of the white man. When people in our village asked why you did not come back, I could not answer. They talked together. They agreed that a Governor who could not control the behavior of a grandson did not have the power to guide the people of our village in their own rights or in their trade with outsiders.

"As Keeper-of-the-Smoke I had special religious duties, such as special prayers to Great Spirit for rains. My prayers were not answered. Drought came. Crops died. Great Spirit was offended. I had turned too far away from the traditions of our people. Now, too late, I see that although there may be some value in some ways of the white man, if our people are to survive we must stay true to our traditions. These ideas that you bring back here, after five years, would destroy the sacredness of our teachings. I now know that Black Fox was wise. You should have stayed in your village with your family."

There was throbbing silence between the two. Pablo spoke. "Our people are bound by superstition and fear. Crops die here from lack of water while we depend for rain upon ceremonies based on legend and the use of charms. While I was away I worked in country that had been dry like this.

Now because the white people there used common sense and knowledge to develop water, the land produces fine crops. These people don't live on tradition and on belief in rain gods." Pablo's voice sounded harsh in his own ears. When had he lost the soft low speech of his people?

His grandfather gave him a long accusing look. Then his words rolled like a heavy boulder down a mountainside. "You will never harm the people of our village with your new beliefs. I could not help you do that even if I wished—for I am no longer Governor. A younger man who stayed here and kept to the ways of our people was chosen by the council to be Governor."

Pablo's breath choked in his throat. "You are still Keeper-of-the-Smoke?"

Tall Bear's mouth twisted with scorn. "For that I am instructing your Younger Brother. He shall not go to the Big School. He will not learn the deceiving language of the white man. Soon he will take my place." Tall Bear got up, went to the house for a moment, then came out and turned toward the trail worn smooth by the feet of generations.

3. Over Dusty Paths

Five years ago Pablo too had walked this trail to help in the gardens. Now he stood looking at the sun-baked desert with its straggling line of adobe houses. A fine dust covered everything. Occasionally a lean dog appeared, searching for morsels of food. Children ran in and out of their homes in aimless play. Nothing had changed, except that everything looked smaller than he remembered. The path seemed narrower and dustier.

He stood incredulous, angry, humiliated. What had they expected when they sent him to the Big School? That traditions and beliefs of his people would not be changed or even dented within him by all he would learn?

He glimpsed his grandmother looking at him from a window. Her figure disappeared. After an intolerably long moment, the door opened and she stepped outside. Putting her hand gently on his shoulder, she said, "I believe Little Badger will go to Pa Vi today. I think you should go with him and see your mother."

Pablo hesitated. "Will she want to see me now?"

Shining Leaf, too, hesitated. She replied only, "You are still her son."

Pablo saw that a car had stopped in the road near the house. Little Badger was waiting there. "I will go, my grandmother," he said. "I have never wished to hurt anyone."

Before his voice could tremble he turned, picked up his suitcase, and walked swiftly to the car of the man who had once helped rescue him.

Neither he nor Little Badger said much during the hot, windy journey by car to Sells.

When they reached Sells, Little Badger said: "We'll leave the car here and borrow a wagon to go to Pa Vi. I can bring back a load of wood from there."

With a start Pablo remembered, this is the way it happened when my grandfather came to take me from Pa Vi to Oidak more than five years ago. He looked around. Sells with its adobe stores and houses had seemed so big and strange to him then.

Now, with a smile he thought, it is only a village.

From Sells the rutted road toward Pa Vi seemed as rough as ever, and the wagon barely crawled along. I could get to Pa Vi faster on foot, he thought.

Finally he said, "Not much change around here since I left."

Little Badger glanced quickly at him. Then in a quiet voice he mentioned a few changes that had taken place here and there. He took particular pains, or so it seemed to Pablo, to say that a small bus now ran once a day, each way, on a gravel road that skirted the desert around Pa Vi. From Little Badger's description Pablo knew that he could reach this bus road by a shortcut from Pa Vi—a walk of about five or six miles across the desert.

4. The Lost One Returns

The purple shadows of dusk were filling the mountain canyons as Little Badger brought Pablo to Pa Vi. The searing wind of the desert had died down and a soft breeze was bringing coolness. When Little Badger stopped to let him out, Pablo smelled the mesquite smoke of the cooking fires and heard the low, laughing chatter of people in their ramadas. These things he had longed for with a deep yearning; he was glad they were unchanged. He drew a deep breath. Would he find other things he loved here unchanged? His experience in Oidak stirred foreboding.

He walked toward the ramada. In the dusk he was not recognized. "My mother. My father. My father's uncle." he said in the Papago tongue.

Everyone stopped talking. Then Black Fox said

236

in a matter-of-fact voice, "The lost one returns."
Red Deer and Gray Owl looked briefly at Pablo,
then turned their eyes away. There were no words
of welcome.

Quick rustlings caused Pablo to turn his head.
Standing where the cook-fire light shone on their
faces were two young people. Could they really
be Younger Brother and Sister? So grown, so tall.
Pablo smiled at them. "Younger Brother, you are
tall—taller than I was when I left to go to the Big
School."

Black-eyed Younger Brother did not smile or
answer. Moving toward them, Pablo looked down
into the lively dark eyes of Younger Sister. "My
Younger Sister," he said quietly. She smiled shyly.
"My Older Brother," she whispered, her eyes
lowered.

His mother spoke. "You will stay here this
night?" She sounds frightened, Pablo thought.

"I will stay this night," he answered softly.

"A canvas blanket is by the tree outside the
ramada," Red Deer told Pablo. Nothing else from
the father after five years of absence.

Sleep did not come to Pablo that night. Old
memories stirred. Now he could only wince and
stare restlessly up at the sky.

Next morning no one in his home spoke to him. When he walked in the village no one hailed him. It was as though he were a total stranger. All about him he felt dislike and fear.

Stiff pride made him stay through the day. He walked over the land. It was cracked and parched —worse than when he left. He looked at the old-fashioned handmade tools. The food he ate with his family, fried bread and beans, was the same as in past years. The sanitation? No better than before.

In the late afternoon he sat down beside Younger Brother in the ramada. "You are learning the rituals of the Keeper-of-the-Smoke?" he asked.

"I know them." Younger Brother answered.

"Do you believe the Great Spirit makes rain come to our land?" Pablo asked.

Younger Brother gave him a black look. "If someone does not offend the Great Spirit, he will give us rain."

Pablo said, "I have learned there are many ways to get water for growing crops. Water can be brought through pipes or tunnels for a long way. It can be found deep in the ground in many places, and brought to where crops need it, and to use for drinking, bathing, and washing clothes."

"Deep in the ground," Younger Brother repeated. His voice was bitter. "Where white men trap and hide it away."

Pablo saw that Younger Brother was striving for self-control. Now the boy spoke again rapidly. "You have been away a long time. People of our village say you have become a white man. In my grandfather's village the people blame and make fun of him because he was not strong enough to keep you—you whom he had chosen to succeed him—from offending Great Spirit." He turned and looked hard into Pablo's eyes. "I wish you had never come back here."

Pablo felt numb. He got up and stood very still, looking out across the desert, feeling himself growing older as his dreams died.

o   o   o

That night after the evening meal, Pablo went outside the ramada to sit by his father and Black Fox. Physical closeness did not draw them together in spirit. No one spoke. Pablo knew they were waiting for him to leave. The only punishment for a grave offense was exile by family and tribe.

He clenched his fists. So let it be that way. But

239

smile. "Many moons ago I found in a shop in a faraway place a basket you had made—" he said slowly. Before he could tell more they saw Black Fox standing in the shadows outside the ramada. Gray Owl gave Pablo a long look and went quickly inside the ramada.

Pablo crossed his arms to cover his face and leaned against a ramada post. Tears stung his eyes. He was unwanted by his family and his tribe. A failure. A thing scorned. A danger feared. His mother's words were final dismissal.

At this point in his darkest despair he felt a soft tug at his sleeve. Younger Sister, he thought. But when he turned, it was Black Fox at his side. Black Fox's face was calm in the moonlight, and free of anger. His tired old eyes were friendly.

"Son-of-my-nephew," he said, "you did not choose the way of life that was pushed upon you. You did not make the decision to go to the Big School and learn to be a white man. It was not you who chose to turn away from the traditions and religion of your tribe—traditions that go back to the beginnings of time."

Pablo, too surprised to answer, stood silent.

Black Fox's eyes looked far into the desert night. He smiled. It was not a happy smile. "Tall Bear is a strong man. His will prevailed. You were sent into the world of the white man. There your inheritance was made a burden and you now think like a white man. This I feared would happen.

"Here in Pa Vi I have kept our traditions and religion and have tried to teach our people to observe them. But I am now an old man and many of our young people will not listen. Younger Sister wants to go away to the Big School. And I have lost the power to keep her thoughts here.

"Younger Brother has kept to the old ways and will go back to Oidak to take the place of Tall Bear as Keeper-of-the-Smoke. But when he has children, will they revere him for holding the beliefs of his ancestors?

"The white man's beliefs are overpowering ours. Gradually the white man is invading our country, taking the things we know and love. I am afraid."

Pablo watched sadly as this bent old warrior turned away and walked slowly into his own home. His time for anger was earlier, thought Pablo. His time for sorrow is now.

5. Example of Coyote

It was done. Pablo knew how they all felt. He could only hurt them if he stayed longer. He picked up his suitcase, took a long look around the familiar old ramada. Then he turned down the path that led from Pa Vi.

He would walk across the desert to the road Little Badger had told him about. He would take the small bus to the highway and there he would catch a big eastbound bus. Soon he would be out of the reservation that was no longer home. Beyond that he had no plan.

As he walked in the clear moonlight, the desert spoke to him with a hundred little voices. A cactus wren muttered sleepily in her cholla nest. A quail clucked reassuringly to her young. There were stirrings in the brush as night creatures, big and small, went stalking for their food. There was the low hooting of an owl and the scamperings and scurryings of tiny legs escaping—sounds Pablo had heard a thousand times in his childhood. Full of thoughts though he was, he came under the desert's spell.

Setting his suitcase down, he squatted on his heels, then gave in to an impulse to stretch out on the ground. Flat on his back, he let his eyes rove among the stars. This, he told himself, was peace. His ears picked up the long wail of a coyote far away. Then he waited for, and heard, another coyote wail in reply.

His mind and feelings were back in simpler days but he knew they couldn't dwell there:

"The uncle of my father has always felt that our traditions are the only thing that can save us from being swallowed by the white man, and he has fought hard to keep even the good ideas of white men away. Now, partly because of what I have done, he is very much afraid. I have learned to question our traditional beliefs. But also I can see now, more than before I left here, how strong they are in our everyday life and how we need them to discipline us and to make us different.

"My grandfather thought otherwise at first. He

245

believed that we could use the white man's good ideas without hurting our old traditions. I think he was right. But traditions were so strong that even my grandfather could not look past them when drought caused suffering. When our people said Eé toy was holding back the rain because Tall Bear's grandson had stayed too long at the Big School, Tall Bear was ready to believe them and to accept their punishment.

"So what did I do when I came back? I caused more trouble for everybody. Tall Bear had hoped I could be a leader. He had told me a leader must have wisdom. But I came back to Oidak without it.

"Because I had gone to the Big School five years and held a couple of jobs, I thought I could tell my people how to use new ways. I don't really know enough about bringing water in this Papago land, but I tried to tell my people that it would work. Some of the old men knew about obstacles that I didn't know. I didn't show respect for their years. I questioned the inner beliefs that are dear to them. This frightened them. I tried to tell instead of asking their opinions. They had to put me away from them."

Pablo's next thought stung him. "They called me a white man. But I am not. What's the word we used in the beet fields? 'Hybrid'—yes, I could be a hybrid."

Pablo's mind flew to the talks he had with Rosie in Laramie.

"Rosie was right in warning me of what might happen if I came back here. She knew I would anger my people—but was she also right in saying I could never be a reservation Indian again?—I think not. Rosie wasn't able to be, but I think I have a better chance. Rosie was a little girl—taken from the reservation by force before she could know much about her people. And when she returned from white schooling she couldn't even speak her native tongue. But I was much older when I started to the Big School. I knew the language and traditions of my people, I will never forget them."

Pablo went over this reasoning several times. Then he remembered with a joyous start that Rosie had also said, "People get power or magic because they believe in themselves and patiently work to keep a goal before them—a goal to reach."

"I have my goal, and I will keep it," resolved Pablo. "My goal is to help my people." Hours passed as he turned his thoughts to plans.

The moonlight was giving way to a stronger light

when a coyote pit-patted out from the nearby brush
and stopped. Using both paws, he started digging in
the sand.

Remembering Tall Bear's words of long ago,
that "coyotes know things we do not understand,"
Pablo now asked, "How can I reach my goal,
Coyote? How?"

Coyote looked up, saw that Pablo was watching,
and dug some more.

This digging and more digging—what could it
mean? Pablo sat up with a start. "Work—that's it,"
he said aloud. "Work and learn as Rosie told me. I
can do that—Coyote, I have your message."

Pablo directed his mind now to Jim Burnett and
his offer to help. "I don't know enough now to
work with the problems of my people, but I can
learn," Pablo told himself. "I will work, go to the
University, study. But I will not forget our traditions. When I really know ways to help my people I will come back. I will try to explain wisely
so they will no longer be divided in their efforts,
because division has held them back. Our people
must learn to work together."

Pablo got to his feet, took a step forward, and
raised his arms to the lifting sun. In his deepest
voice, as he had heard Black Fox and Tall Bear

many times before him, Pablo chanted his own sun-rise call:

"The sun rises over this land.
The soil is hungry,
The water is scarce,
But the voice is joyful,
The heart is happy,
For the wish is strong,
The wish of desert people,
The wish for the magic of water."

Pablo stood awhile with head bowed toward the east. Then he turned to face the far-off Babo-quivari, whose top was now alight with the new day. He spoke aloud to Eé toy, dwelling up there.

"Great Spirit," he said in a surge of awe, "I promise to come back."

With a light heart he picked up his suitcase and walked to catch the bus.

About the Author

HAZEL FREDERICKSEN, although this is her first work of fiction, has written numerous professional articles in the field of social work and a textbook on child welfare.

From childhood she has known American Indians. They used to visit at her family's ranch in Colorado. From that acquaintance grew a concern that led her into training as a teacher, psychologist and psychiatric social worker. These professional skills, in turn, involved her in an inter-departmental study for the U.S. Department of Health, the Bureau of Indian Affairs, and the U.S. Bureau on the Health and Welfare of Indian Children — an effort by the three bureaus to collaborate rather than compete over the national problems we have delegated to them.

Providing for Indian culture in an overall technological society is no easy problem for society to delegate. Mrs. Fredericksen's feeling is that Indian talents have long been wasted due to White America's failure to listen and learn.

About the Artist

JOHN SHERRILL AUNE HOUSER is a South Dakotan by birth and a resident of Arizona. Though he supports himself and his wife as a painter and fine artist, his degree at Lewis and Clark College in Oregon was in science as well as in art. He has retained his interest in economics and anthropology, particularly in relation to the problems of subcultures here and abroad. He did graduate work in art at UCLA and worked abroad on a Greenshields International Fellowship — France, Denmark, Italy, Holland, Spain, Morocco, and Mexico being included in his travels.

For this book he supplemented his knowledge of the Southwest by frequent visits to the Papago reservation.